PLAYS TO ENJOY

LITERATURE TO ENJOY
Stories to Enjoy
Poems to Enjoy
Plays to Enjoy
Readings to Enjoy

LITERATURE TO REMEMBER
Stories to Remember
Poems to Remember
Plays to Remember
Readings to Remember

Revised Edition

PLAYS
TO
ENJOY

RAYMOND PICOZZI

Associate Professor of Elementary Education
Rhode Island College
Providence, Rhode Island

THE MACMILLAN COMPANY,
COLLIER-MACMILLAN LIMITED, LONDON

ACKNOWLEDGMENTS

For permission to reprint copyright material in this volume, grateful acknowledgment is made to the following:

Ashley-Famous Agency, Inc.: For *Grandpa and the Statue*, by Arthur Miller. Copyright 1945 by Arthur Miller. Reprinted by permission of Ashley-Famous Agency, Inc.

Walter H. Baker Company: For *Dr. Heidegger's Experiment*, by Nathaniel Hawthorne, dramatized by Marvin G. Robinson. Reprinted from *From Story to Stage*. Copyright 1946 by Walter H. Baker Company.

CAUTION: For professional rights, radio, television, or any mechanical rights, write to Baker's Plays, 100 Summer Street, Boston, Massachusetts 02110.

Milton Geiger: For *In the Fog*.

Harcourt, Brace & World, Inc., and the Estate of John Van Druten: For an excerpt from *I Remember Mama*, by John Van Druten. Copyright 1944, 1945, by John Van Druten. Reprinted by permission of Harcourt, Brace & World, Inc.

Jerome Lawrence and Robert E. Lee: For *Inside a Kid's Head*. Copyright 1945 by Jerome Lawrence and Robert E. Lee.

CAUTION: Professionals and amateurs are hereby warned that *Inside*

(*acknowledgments continued on page 170*)

Illustrated by Vivian Berger, Publisher's Art.

The Macmillan Company
Collier-Macmillan Canada, Ltd., Toronto, Ontario

Printed in the United States of America

Contents

ABOUT READING PLAYS

Since early times, plays have been a wonderful form of written and spoken communication. The ancient Greeks and Romans used to watch plays in large out-of-door theatres. We still can see plays performed out-of-doors, especially in the summertime, but we can also see them in theatres, in auditoriums, in movies, and on television. Today we have plays with music and dancing, plays with humor—all reflecting different sides of life.

You have undoubtedly seen a play at one time or another. Perhaps you saw the play in school, at a theatre, in a tent out in a field, or on television right in your own home. While it is marvelous to experience the thrill and spectacle of seeing a play, it is not always possible to do this as often as you would like to. You can, however, enjoy plays as often as you wish by reading them. Reading plays can be as enjoyable and satisfying as seeing them, especially if you read carefully and know a few basic facts.

A playwright creates his story or plot by showing you the words, actions, gestures, and facial expressions of his characters. The characters are the people in the play. You share the lives of these people, and as you become involved with them, the play becomes a real, exciting experience.

When you start to read a play, look at the list of the characters. Read the names of the characters, and also the brief bits of information about them that sometimes appear beside their names. See if any of them are related to each other. Then begin to use your imagination to see and hear these people in your mind. As you read the play, picture in your mind how the characters might look, how old they are, what their manners and personalities are like, and how they feel and act toward one another.

Notice, too, the description of the scene, the place where the play happens. Then you will be able to create a background for your characters—a home, a ship, a street, a forest, a dreamland castle, or whatever is described to put the characters in a realistic (or imaginary) place.

The play begins—the characters speak. The words that the characters say are called the dialogue. Look for clues in the dialogue which will tell you more about the personalities, feelings, and ideas of the characters. Also watch for hints about the action and the purpose of the plot. The plot is the series of events that create the action and excitement in the play. In every play you read or see, there is a certain time when the action and dialogue reach a high exciting point. This is the high spot or important moment in the play. This time in the plot has a name—it is called the climax or turning point. From this point on, the problems of the characters, and the main ideas of the play, are worked out in one way or another. Fairly soon after the climax, the play comes smoothly to an end.

Most of the plays in this book are one-act plays. In a one-act play, the main actions and ideas are usually shown rather quickly, since time and space are limited. As you read the plays, watch for hints and necessary information, and try to spot the important actions and ideas as soon as they are presented to you. Notice how the author manages to fit all his people and events neatly together, even in a very short play.

As you read a play, allow yourself time to think about the characters' words and actions. Think over what each character says and does. How does the character look as he says these words? What is he doing? Where is he? How are the other characters reacting to his words? How are these words important to the action and ideas which are developing in the play? Search constantly for hints as to what is going to be said and done next. Keep your imagination working constantly to create the scene in your mind. You can laugh, cry, gasp, sigh, or wonder as you read a play, for in your mind you have created a living, colorful, vivid performance.

The play is an art form used by man to interpret his world. It is not just an activity for entertainment, but rather a vivid, living document of people's constant search for meaning and purpose. By reading plays, you can gain whole new ideas, not only about literature and the theatre, but also about life.

INSIDE A KID'S HEAD

JEROME LAWRENCE

and

ROBERT E. LEE

INSIDE A KID'S HEAD

Look at the boy or girl sitting in front of you. Can you tell what he is thinking? What might happen if you could?

The play *Inside a Kid's Head* gives you just such a view of a boy's thoughts. It takes you on a guided tour through the busy brain of twelve-year-old Ritchie Price.

The playwrights lead this tour by using only *sound*, for this is a radio play. A radio play cannot show you pictures in technicolor and cinemascope. But through speech, music, and special sound effects, the playwrights guide your imagination so that you can hear and "see" the play in your mind. And because a radio play does not depend on heavy stage props or expensive scenery, it can carry your imagination quickly from one time and place to another, or from real-life scenes to imaginary ones. These scenes will sometimes change quickly, so be alert!

To follow the sound clues, you will need to understand some special radio terms. A few examples: "up" means louder, and "down" means softer. A sound that "fades out" becomes gradually softer and disappears. A "bridge" is a musical connection between two separate scenes or speeches. A "filter" effect makes a voice seem muffled, as if coming over a telephone. You can probably guess most of the radio terms from their use and position in the play. If any are difficult for you, use the dictionary for help.

Tourists now departing at Gate 7—all aboard!

CHARACTERS

ANNOUNCER

GUIDE

MAN and WOMAN in tourist party

VOICES 1, 2, 3 and 4 in Ritchie's brain

MISS LUDLOW

RITCHIE

KING JOHN

BARONS 1, 2 and 3

MARY JANE

MAC

MOTHER

FATHER

J. D. WINKLER (same voice as King John)

BILLY WINKLER

RADIO VOICE (fight announcer)

TRAINER (same voice as Mac)

MINUTEMAN (same voice as Father)

VOICES 1 and 2 in crowd of townspeople

ANNOUNCER. INSIDE A KID'S HEAD. . . . This personally conducted tour through the brain of a twelve-year-old boy was arranged in script form by Jerome Lawrence and Robert E. Lee. Ladies and gentlemen, are you ready now? Very good. Right this way, please. Just follow the guide!

(*Music: "Inside a Kid's Head" theme . . . establish, then down and out behind*)

(*Slight echo through this scene*)
(*Group milling about*)

GUIDE. We are now standing inside the brain of—uh—Ritchie Price. This is not usually included in the fifty-five cent tour, but—excuse me, sir! Don't stand too close to those nerve centers—high voltage, you know!

MAN. Oh—sorry.

GUIDE. Right now Ritchie is in his history class in Grade 7B at Patrick Henry Junior High School. We are standing at the medulla oblongata, looking up into the cerebellum.

WOMAN. Pardon me, guide—but what is all that over there? It looks like wool.

GUIDE. That *is* wool, madame. This boy has been woolgathering quite a bit lately. Uh . . . you will notice that the walls here are lined with gray matter, which absorbs any ideas that may be floating about.

(*Slide whistle—zoop, zoop!*)

WOMAN. Oh!

MAN. What was that, guide?

GUIDE. That was just an idea going in one ear and out the other! And look!—over there!

WOMAN. Where?

GUIDE. Peeking out from behind those brain cells! It's a little date.

MAN. A what?

GUIDE. A date. It's so hazy, I can't quite make out the year . . . ! Oh, yes! It's 1215 A.D.!

(*Quick ascending "zoop" of slide whistle*)

ALL (*Chuckle*).

GUIDE. Cute little fellow, wasn't he!

MAN. Are all dates as shy as that?

GUIDE. No, I'm afraid this boy doesn't have a very good memory for dates.

WOMAN. Guide, what did you say this boy's name was?

GUIDE. Ritchie Price, ma'am.

(*Footsteps*)

Now, if you'll just follow me up this passageway, we'll have a look at the cerebrum. Oh! careful you don't slip into that crevice!

WOMAN. My, it's deep! What is it, guide?

GUIDE. Lapse of memory—a big one, too!

(*Hum of automatic, repetitive machinery—such as adding machines*)

We're now coming into the cerebrum—the largest section of the brain. On the right, you see the master control panel for the automatic functions—such as heartbeats, digestion, breathing, and so forth.

VOICE 1 (*filter*). Inhale!

(*Gasp of breath intake*)

Exhale!

(*Gasp of breath exhaled*)

Inhale!

(*Gasp of breath intake*)

Exhale!

(*Breath exhaled*)

WOMAN. That must be the breathing mechanism!

GUIDE. That's right, ma'am. And here's the digestion control.

VOICE 2 (*through a speaking tube*). Four more licorice drops coming down the epiglottis.

VOICE 3 (*filter*). Okay. Better turn on a little more gastric juice.

VOICE 2 (*speaking tube*). Right, chief!

(*Buzz, as of interoffice communication—click!*)

VOICE 3 (*filter*). Master control. Go ahead.

VOICE 4 (*sharp filter*). Stomach calling. (*Pained*) Look, chief! I'm gonna be upset if this eating between meals isn't cut out! I haven't even digested those peanut-butter sandwiches that came down for lunch! We gotta get some rest down here!

VOICE 3 (*filter*). Well, I'll shoot a memo up to the "common-sense" department, and see if we can't get 'em to conserve on the food intake. But we haven't been getting much co-operation from common sense lately . . . (*Fading*) Do the best you can.

VOICE 4. O.K., chief.

(*Click of switch*)

WOMAN. Isn't that wonderful?

GUIDE. Yes, it's quite a complicated apparatus. Now, folks, we've installed an observation booth on the second floor of the cranium. Right up these stairs. (*Footsteps*) From this booth, you can see and hear everything that goes on in this boy's dome. Through these double doors, please . . .

(*Sound of double doors*)

WOMAN. Oh, this is nice . . . !

MAN. Plush chairs, and everything. Can we smoke?

GUIDE. No, Board of Health says no smoking. Might cause a fever. Just a moment . . . I'll turn this loudspeaker on the main thinking channel. . . .

(*Squeals . . . heterodyne . . . then:*)

MISS LUDLOW (*fading in, but remaining slightly off*). And, children, don't forget that up to this time King John was the *absolute monarch* of England. Anything he said was *law!*

GUIDE (*close*). That's his history teacher talking.

MISS LUDLOW (*continuing*). But King John wasn't a good king. He mistreated his subjects, and that's why his barons made him sign the Great Charter. (*Blob of static*) Now, close your history books, children (*More static, squeals*)— and we'll take up the General Science lesson for today.

GUIDE. Reception isn't very good. I'm afraid this boy Ritchie Price isn't paying much attention to his teacher.

(*Music: Bong! Vibraphone, octaves, struck with hard mallets, plus echo*)

(*Fading off*) Oh-oh! The imagination is coming in on the

same wave length! This ought to be interesting . . .

RITCHIE (*aged twelve—fading in*). Now look here, King John! You've been actin' awful bossy lately! An' we barons are gettin' pretty sick of it!

KING JOHN (*firmly*). What dost thou propose, Sir Ritchie? Thou hast no right to challenge the King of England!

RITCHIE. Well, now, your Majesty, we barons have been talkin' this over, jes' between ourselves. An' we come to the conclusion the people oughta have somethin' to say about what's goin' on. How about it, boys?

BARON 1. Yes! Sir Ritchie speaks aright!

BARON 2. We are with him!

BARON 3. To the last man!

MARY JANE (*aged twelve*). Please, father! Why don't you do as Sir Ritchie asks? He's so handsome!

KING JOHN. This is none of thy concern, Princess Mary Jane! My liegemen, this is *treason!*

RITCHIE. Jes' get down off your high horse, King John! All we're askin' yuh to do is put your name on this hunk of paper, so's folks don't have to worry about you not treatin' 'em right. Now, I happen to have a fountain pen right here in my suit of armor. If you'll jes' sign on the dotted line . . .

KING JOHN. I refuse! Thou art traitors! All of you!

RITCHIE (*very matter-of-fact*). We mean business, King John! You better sign, or we'll have to get tough!

BARON 1. Yes, sign!

BARON 2. Sign, your Majesty!

BARON 3. We demand that thou sign the charter!

KING JOHN (*riding over the voices*). Does no man remain loyal to his king?

RITCHIE. We're loyal, King John! But we jes' don't like the

idea of you having your own way all the time. We want some say-so, too! That's only fair!

MARY JANE. Sir Ritchie is right! Sign, father!

BARON 1. Yes! If you want to keep your throne!

KING JOHN. Very well, Sir Ritchie. Give me the pen.

(*Scratch of pen*)

KING JOHN (*pouting like an adolescent*). There! Take your old paper!

BARONS (*cheers*).

MARY JANE. Sir Ritchie—you're *so* wonderful!

RITCHIE (*tossing it off*). Oh, it was nothing . . . ! (*Over cheers*) Gentlemen! (*As if springing a dramatic piece of information*) Gentlemen! We shall call this—the *Magna Charta!*

BARON 1. Three cheers for Sir Ritchie!

ALL. Hurrah for Sir Ritchie! Ritchie! Ritchie!

(*Simultaneous cross-fade into:*)

MISS LUDLOW (*fading in, overlapping*). Ritchie! Ritchie! Ritchie!

RITCHIE. Huh? (*Coming to*) Yes, Miss Ludlow?

MISS LUDLOW. Will you stop daydreaming long enough to answer the question I just asked?

RITCHIE (*groping*). Why . . . uh . . . uh . . . (*Timidly*) King John . . . ?

CLASS (*laughter*).

MISS LUDLOW (*after laughter subsides*). In fourteen years of teaching, that is the first time a pupil ever told me that King John invented the sewing machine!

CLASS (*laughter*).

(*Electric bell rings, scrape of feet*)

MISS LUDLOW. Wait, class! For tomorrow, study Chapter

Eight in your General Science book. Class dismissed.
(*Hurried shuffle of feet. Immediate babbling of released kids*)
(*Calling*) Oh, Ritchie!

RITCHIE (*gulping*). Yes, ma'am?

MISS LUDLOW. Ritchie, what do you think we should do with a boy who doesn't pay attention in class?

RITCHIE. I don't know, ma'am . . .

MISS LUDLOW. Do you think we should give him a note to take home to his parents?

RITCHIE (*meekly*). Do we have to do anything that—er—severe?

MISS LUDLOW (*as pen scratches*). I'm afraid so. There you are. (*Envelope folded*) I want you to take this home—have your father sign it, and bring it back to me.

RITCHIE (*crestfallen*). Yes, ma'am.
(*Slow footsteps*)
(*Suddenly*) Mary Jane! (*Shouting*) Hey! Mary Jane!
(*Running footsteps . . . up to walk*)

MARY JANE. Go away, silly. I don't want to be seen walking with you.

RITCHIE. Gee whiz, Mary Jane. What's the matter?

MARY JANE. 'Cause you're silly—that's what you are! Why don't you ever study your lessons?

RITCHIE. I do, but—(*frustrated*) I jes' forget—or something!

MARY JANE. You needn't ask me to walk home with you. Billy Winkler's already asked me.

RITCHIE (*contemptuously*). Him? (*Disappointed*) Oh, gee. Gee whiz!

(*Music: Fade in "Inside a Kid's Head" theme*)

(*Slight echo through the following*)

WOMAN (*startled*). Oh! What's that, guide?

GUIDE (*calmly*). Keep your seats, ladies and gentlemen! There's nothing to worry about. That low gray fog you see rolling in from the cerebellum is nothing but gloom— *pure gloom!*

(*Music builds into a bridge—down and out*)

MOTHER. Ritchie, just wait until your father sees this note from Miss Ludlow.

RITCHIE. Do we hafta show it to him?

MOTHER (*reading*). "Complete lack of classroom spirit," it says. Your father'll be furious.

RITCHIE. Maybe we hadn't oughta bother him, when he's so worried about the election.

MOTHER. When those boys and girls go home and tell their folks the kind of boy you are, do you think they'll vote for Daddy next Tuesday?

RITCHIE (*hopelessly*). I don't know.

MOTHER (*fussy*). Good heavens, your father'll be home any minute. Be sure to brush your hair and clean your fingernails, Ritchie. Before dinner! Your father's invited the Winklers over.

RITCHIE. Billy, too? Is *he* coming?

MOTHER. Yes. And I want you to be a little gentleman.

RITCHIE. Oh, nuts!

MOTHER. After all, Mr. Winkler is one of the most important men in the county.

RITCHIE (*almost to himself*). He's fat—that's what.

MOTHER. And if we want daddy to be elected state assemblyman, we'll have to be very nice to the Winklers. (*Suddenly*) Good heavens! The carpet in here is all scuffed up again! Ritchie, get out the vacuum cleaner and run it over once. (*Fading*) The Winklers are so fussy . . .

RITCHIE (*tired of it all*). Okay, mom.

(*Closet door opens, rattle of vacuum cleaner*)

(*Singing to himself, a song of his own composition*)

Billy Winkler. He's a stinkler.

Billy Winkler. He's a stinkler.

(*Vacuum cleaner zooms to start . . . back and forth rhythmically, with vicious tugs . . . on mike, then away from mike, then back on again . . . continue behind the following:*)

RITCHIE (*muttering to himself*). Now it's vacuum cleaners. Vacuum cleaners and sewing machines. Who cares about them! Someday I'll invent somethin' BIG—like an airplane! (*Rhythm with the vacuum cleaner*) Zoom! Zoom! Zoom! Zoom!

(*Music: Vibraphone—Bong!—as before . . .*)

(*Cross fade from vacuum cleaner through to crude airplane motor idling . . . coughs . . . conks out*)

(*Sighs*). Hm. I guess there's dirt in the carburetor. We'll have to take the motor apart.

MAC (*fading*). Say, fellows—there's a lady here who wants to meet you. She *says* her name's Miss Ludlow.

RITCHIE. Better watch out, Mac. She might be an enemy spy!

MAC. Naw, I think she's harmless. Miss Ludlow, these are the greatest inventors in the world! I want you to meet—the Wright Brothers! This is the oldest—Ritchie Wright. . . .

RITCHIE. Glad to know you, ma'am.

MAC. And this is his younger brother—Ritchie.

MISS LUDLOW (*awed*). How do you do?

RITCHIE (*Gary Cooper modesty*). We'd like t' give yuh more of our time, ma'am—but my brother an' me are busy inventin' the flyin' machine. Got that carburetor cleaned out, Ritchie?

RITCHIE (*off, changes his voice only slightly*). You bet, Ritchie!

RITCHIE (*on mike*). Okay, Mac! Crank her up!

MAC (*off*). Contact?

RITCHIE (*on mike*). Contact?

(*Old-fashioned propeller wound up—airplane motor catches*)

RITCHIE. Okay! We're going to take off now!

MAC (*off*). Good luck, boys!

RITCHIE. Here we go!

(*Motor zooms up*)

MAC (*shouting*). Boy, look at that cloud of dust!

(*Plane takes off*)

RITCHIE (*slightly off*). Congratulations, Ritchie! It flies!

RITCHIE (*on*). You know what let's call our invention, Ritchie?

RITCHIE (*slightly off*). *What*, Ritchie?

RITCHIE (*triumphantly*). The *airplane!!!!!*

(*Full airplane motor up to dominate scene—hold—then cross-fade into sound of vacuum cleaner running with bag disconnected—lots of fan gust*)

FATHER (*fading in, coughing*). What the devil are you doing, Ritchie? (*Coughs*) Put the bag back on that vacuum cleaner!

MOTHER (*fading in*). What's happened? (*Sees*) Ohhhhhh! Dust! All over my nice clean living room!!!!

FATHER. For Pete's sake, shut that thing off!

RITCHIE (*obediently*). Yes, father.

(*Cut vacuum cleaner*)

FATHER (*simmering*). Racing around the room, spraying dust all over the place!

MOTHER. Look at those piano keys!

FATHER. What will the Winklers think? The one night I wanted to impress them, and the house looks like a pigsty! (*Door bell, off*)

FATHER. Good lord! There they are!

(*Music: Bridge, segue into "Inside a Kid's Head" theme*)

(*Slight echo on the following*)

WOMAN. I say there—guide!

GUIDE. Yes, ma'am?

WOMAN. What's happening now?

GUIDE. Well, I think they're at dinner. I can't tell exactly . . .

MAN. Guide, look at the window of the observation booth! They're all covered with frost.

GUIDE. Ritchie's father is probably giving him an icy stare. That forms a glacial condition in the brain cells—and probably his thought stream is frozen.

(*Music: out*)

(*Dinner effects . . . dishes, etc.*)

RITCHIE (*meekly*). May I have another helping of dessert, please?

FATHER (*icily*). You may *not!* (*Then warmly*) As I was saying, J.D., we all know how badly the state highway commission has been run. Now, if I'm elected state assemblyman, that graft is going to be stopped.

WINKLER (*a pompous character—we've met him before as King John*). A lofty sentiment, Price.

FATHER. Now, I have facts on this highway swindle that'll blow the opposition to bits. It's all typed out, here in this article. (*Taps the paper significantly*) But Jeff Green's newspaper won't print it—he's on the other side of the fence, politically.

WINKLER (*clears his throat*).

FATHER. What's the matter, J.D.?

WINKLER. Well . . . there seems to be a little dust in my coffee.

MOTHER (*quickly*). Oh, I'll get you another cup right away, Mr. Winkler! (*Fading*) Gracious!

BILLY (*a nasty kid*). What are you kickin' about, pop! There was dust all over my mashed potatoes.

WINKLER. Be quiet, Billy.

FATHER (*a little self-conscious laugh*). Well, as I was saying, here's my idea, J.D. Get an appropriation from the party funds to print up and mail a copy of this exposé to every voter in the county. The election'd be in the bag!

MOTHER. There'll be some more coffee along in a minute. Why don't we all go into the living room and have it there?

(*Shuffling of chairs*)

FATHER. Good idea. (*Pointedly*) Ritchie, you take Billy up to your room and show him your electric train.

BILLY (*superiorly*). Oh. Does he still play with electric trains?

WINKLER. Run along, Billy.

BILLY (*bored*). Okay.

FATHER (*fading off*). Now, it may run into some money, J.D. —but as I see it, it's the only sure way to get the votes we need.

RITCHIE (*dully*). Come on.

(*Footsteps, up stairs*)

BILLY. Don't you folks ever clean your house?

RITCHIE. Sure we do!

BILLY. *We* got a maid that comes in every day!

RITCHIE. Aw, who wants an old maid?

(*Door opens*)

RITCHIE. This is my room.

BILLY. Gee, it's small. (*Let's get it over with!*) Let's see your train.

RITCHIE. It's all set up over here. (*Getting enthusiastic*) It's got a variable speed rheostat, automatic signals, an' it'll stop on a dime! Watch!
(*Purr of toy train . . . then stops*)
See? Isn't that keen?

BILLY. Nah. It's punk. That's for kids. What else you got?

RITCHIE (*grimly*). I got some boxing gloves. Here. Try 'em on.

BILLY. I don't like boxing gloves.

RITCHIE. C'mon. I'll show yuh somethin'.

BILLY. I don't wanna.

RITCHIE. You said you didn't like kid stuff. Well, this ain't kid stuff. Come on, put up your dukes!

BILLY. Hey, wait a minute! Don't you hurt me!

RITCHIE. It's easy, see? You lead with your right—an' then with your left. Like this . . . one-two—one-two . . . one-two . . .

(*Music: Vibraphone—bong! As before*)

(*Fade in terrific cheers, as at Madison Square Garden . . . Thud of blows landing, heavy breathing of boxers*)

RADIO VOICE. A right to the body and a left to the head! And another! And another! It's the old one-two, one-two! Dempsey's in rare form tonight! It's the fight of his life! (*A big shout from the crowd*) Ooohhhh! The challenger just launched a terrific left to Dempsey's chin! He's reeling—! The champ's against the ropes—!
(*Fight gong*)
And there's the bell that ends the round! The seconds are helping Dempsey back to his corner . . .

(Fade slightly)

(Crowd up and down)

TRAINER *(same voice as Mac)*. How are yuh, Ritchie? Are yuh all right, boy?

RITCHIE. It was nothing, Mac! Gimme that towel!

TRAINER. Don't forget—Ritchie Dempsey has never lost a fight!

RITCHIE. Don't worry, Mac—I won't let you down!

TRAINER. It's not just the world's heavyweight championship that's at stake—or that million-dollar purse!—but Mary Jane has promised to walk home from school with the winner of this fight!!!

RITCHIE *(aglow)*. Did she really say that?

TRAINER. And what's more—she's out there in the audience now, cheering for you!

RITCHIE *(melodramatically)*. Mary Jane! Here???????

MARY JANE *(floating over the crowd)*. Hurray for Ritchie Dempsey!

(Fight gong)

RITCHIE *(gritting, under his breath)*. Let me at that Billy Firpo!

(Crowd cheers up)

RADIO VOICE. They're coming out of their corners . . .

(Terrific sock! Crowd goes crazy)

Ooooohhhhh! With the first punch of the round, Ritchie Dempsey knocks the challenger *out cold!!!*

(Crowd up)

Mr. Dempsey! Won't you say something to our radio audience?

RITCHIE *(with magnanimous modesty)*. Gentlemen! I am happy to be the *heavyweight champion of the world!!!!*

(Swell crowd up full, then cut abruptly on door slam)

FATHER. Ritchie! What's happened?

WINKLER. What's Billy doing there on the floor? Wake up, son—wake up!

RITCHIE *(weakly)*. We was just . . . playin' . . .

FATHER. The boy's out cold! Mother, get some smelling salts!

MOTHER *(fading)*. Oh, dear . . .

BILLY *(coming to)*. Huh? What happened?

WINKLER *(up, to mother)*. Never mind, Mrs. Price. He's coming to.

(To Billy) Are you hurt, son?

BILLY. My chin hurts. *(Tattletale) He* hit me on the chin!

FATHER. Ritchie!

WINKLER *(crisply)*. Would you mind getting our coats! I'd better get the boy home.

FATHER *(panicky)*. But, J.D.! What about the election? What about—?

WINKLER. We'll have to forget the whole thing for now. And, Price—if that was *my* boy, he'd get a good—*talking to!!!!*

(Door opens)

Good night.

MOTHER }
FATHER } *(weakly)*. Good night.

(Door slams)

(There is a menacing pause)

RITCHIE *(filling the void)*. I—I guess Mr. Winkler was sorta mad . . . wasn't he, father?

FATHER. Ritchie.

RITCHIE. Yes, Dad?

FATHER *(not raising his voice, very calmly)*. You wanted me to·be elected state assemblyman next Tuesday, didn't you?

RITCHIE. Sure, Dad.

FATHER. There isn't a chance now. Mr. Winkler was the only man who could get that article of mine published and circulated.

RITCHIE (*meekly*). Would you like to take away my allowance for a week?

FATHER. Ritchie, your mother and I are going to give you just one more chance. If I hear of your misbehaving just *once* again—something *drastic* is going to happen.

RITCHIE (*to himself*). Gee whiz.

FATHER. Is there any aspirin, Ella?

MOTHER. Yes . . . in the medicine chest.

FATHER. I'm going to lie down for a while. (*Fading*) This is one of the most hectic evenings I've ever spent.

(*Door opens and closes*)

RITCHIE (*with a gulp*). Mom?

MOTHER. Yes, Ritchie?

RITCHIE. Did you give Dad that note from Miss Ludlow yet?

MOTHER. I gave it to him, but he just stuffed it in his pocket. I don't think he's read it yet.

RITCHIE. You don't, huh? (*Overly innocent*) Mom . . . was it his *suit* coat pocket or his *over*coat pocket?

(*Music: "Inside a Kid's Head" theme . . . down behind*)

(*Echo on the following*)
(*Fire gong, clanging violently*)

WOMAN. Good gracious, guide! What's that?

GUIDE. That's a three-alarm warning from the conscience.

MAN. What's going on?

WOMAN. Is there any danger?

GUIDE. Can't tell exactly, yet. Evidently young Ritchie's up to something he shouldn't be doing. I haven't heard a racket like that from his conscience since he cribbed in an arithmetic exam two years ago.

(Fire gong becomes fainter and more muffled)

WOMAN. Say, guide! Isn't it getting fainter?

GUIDE *(with a sigh)*. Yes—I'm afraid he isn't paying much attention to it.

(Gong cuts off)

MAN. Oh-oh! What's happened?

GUIDE. Let's tune in on the visual channel and see what he's up to.

(Heterodyne squeals, static, etc.)

(Shocked whisper) Do you see what he's doing? He's sneaking into his father's closet . . . he's reaching into his father's coat pocket . . . he's groping around in the dark . . .

WOMAN *(little fearful gasp)*.

GUIDE. He's taking an envelope out of the pocket and slipping it under his sweater.

(Sliding chairs, jarring of heavy footsteps)

(Music goes into jarring, out-of-beat rhythm)

MAN
WOMAN } *(Gasps, as if being shaken up)*.

GUIDE. Hang onto your chairs, ladies and gentlemen! There's nothing to worry about! Ritchie's just going downstairs *three steps at a time!!!!*

(Music swells into bridge . . . down into:)

(Door opens. Fade in hum-clack of linotype machine)

RITCHIE *(puffing)*. Hi, Mac!

MAC *(noncommittal)*. Hi, Ritchie.

(Treats Ritchie as an adult and an equal. He alone understands Ritchie's problems. He's laconic, slow-speaking)

(Linotype continues for a while . . . then shuts off)

RITCHIE *(professionally)*. Puttin' the paper to bed, Mac?

MAC. Yep.

RITCHIE. Got much more to linotype?

MAC. Just the editorials. Then we're all washed up.

RITCHIE. Will yuh let me type some?

MAC. Mebbe. (*Pause*) Well, spill it.

RITCHIE. Huh?

MAC. Spill it. What's on your mind?

RITCHIE. Oh. (*With a heavy sigh*) Gosh, Mac! Nobody under-stands me—except you! You're the only friend I've got in the world!

MAC. Trouble at home?

RITCHIE (*wearily*). Trouble every place! I guess I dinged my dad's chances of bein' state assemblyman . . . I got bawled out at school . . . Mary Jane doesn't like me any more . . . an' everything . . . !

MAC. Mmmmm-hmmmm. Where was yuh runnin' from just now?

RITCHIE. Home. (*Then blurting out the whole story in a burst of words*) I said King John invented the sewing machine, an' Miss Ludlow gave me a note to take home to my dad, an' all kinds of terrible things happened at home, so I took the note out of my dad's pocket so he wouldn't see it . . . and . . . well . . . here I am!

MAC (*narrowing his eyes*). Yuh mean yuh went through your pa's pockets?

RITCHIE. I didn't steal anything! I jes' *borrowed* the note for a while . . . so's he wouldn't see it and have more to worry about.

MAC. Lemme see that note.

RITCHIE. Here.

(*Rustle of paper*)

MAC (*reading*). Hm. (*Looking up*) Miss Ludlow write this?

RITCHIE. Yeah.

MAC (*reading*). "I charge . . . that the state highway commission . . . is rife with graft and corruption . . ."

RITCHIE (*sunk*). Holy Jumpin' Jupiter!!!! I got the wrong paper!!

MAC. I kinda wondered if Miss Ludlow was goin' into politics.

RITCHIE. Oh, Mac—my dad'll skin me! Everything's wrong now! (*Almost in tears*) Gee whiz, Mac! What'll I do????

MAC. Look. Things'll work out all right. What you gotta do is get your mind offa your troubles. Why don't you go over an' knock out a few lines on the other linotype?

RITCHIE (*getting out of his sulk*). Can I? Honest?

MAC. Sure. But watch out you don't get a shock from that Square-D switch on the baseboard.

RITCHIE. Thanks, Mac—gee! Thanks!

(*Hum of linotype starting. Clack of keys*)

Gosh! Now what'll I write?

(*Music: Vibraphone—bong! As before, as Ritchie goes off into another dream*)

RITCHIE (*calling*). Oh, Miss Mary Jane!

MARY JANE (*off*). Yes, Mr. Franklin?

RITCHIE. Bring your notebook in here. I want to give you some dictation for Poor Ritchie's Almanac.

MARY JANE (*fading in*). Yes, Mr. Franklin.

RITCHIE. Take a maxim! "A penny saved is a penny earned." How do you like that, Miss Mary Jane?

MARY JANE. A lofty sentiment, Mr. Franklin.

RITCHIE. You may call me Ritchie, if you like.

MARY JANE. Oh, thank you . . . Ritchie!

RITCHIE. And here's another one that I thought of yesterday afternoon while I was inventing the rocking chair. "A stitch in time saves nine."

MARY JANE. Oh, you're so clever, Ritchie Franklin.

RITCHIE. Take those down to the pressroom—and see that they get in this issue of Poor Ritchie's Almanac.

MARY JANE. Yes, Mr. Franklin.

RITCHIE. Hmmmm. I have a free hour. What do you suppose I ought to invent?

MARY JANE. *You're* the clever one, Mr. Franklin.

RITCHIE (*a sudden idea*). I know! It's an idea I had while I was in France last year buying Louisiana! Thought I'd call it the harmonica!

MARY JANE (*fading*). I'll take these maxims right down to the print shop.

RITCHIE. Very well.

(*Door closes*)

(*Considering*) Now, let me see . . .

(*Whistles while there is a bit of hammering, scraping of tools*)

(*Door opens*)

MARY JANE (*fading in*). Is there anything else, Mr. Franklin?

RITCHIE. Well, it's all finished! Listen!

(*Quick run, up and down the scale, on a harmonica*)

MARY JANE. Oh, it's *wonderful!* You're so *clever*, Ritchie Franklin!

RITCHIE (*Spencer Tracy modesty*). It's nothing, really . . .

(*Loud hammering on the door*)

(*Calling*) Come in!

(*Door opens*)

MINUTEMAN (*the voice is his father's*). Mr. Franklin! I have a scoop for Poor Ritchie's Almanac! (*Very excited*)

RITCHIE. Now, just calm down, young man, and tell me what this is all about.

MINUTEMAN (*very excitedly*). Mr. Franklin, I charge that

the Continental Congress is rife with graft and corruption! Here—this paper will explain everything!

RITCHIE. Miss Mary Jane, would you please hand me my bifocals? Thank you. Hmmmm. Why, this will blow the opposition to bits!!!

MINUTEMAN. Every voter in the American colonies should see a copy of this exposé! And you're the only man who can publish and circulate it—in Poor Ritchie's Almanac!

RITCHIE. It's very fortunate that yesterday I invented the linotype machine. Otherwise, we could never get this out in time for today's issue. Come with me!

(*Footsteps . . . Door opens and closes . . . fade in hum-clack of linotype machine*)

MINUTEMAN. What an amazing machine! Where did you ever get the idea?

RITCHIE. It came to me like a flash while I was signing the Declaration of Independence. Give me that exposé. I'll set it up myself!

(*Linotype machine runs for a while . . . Then sudden clap of thunder, off*)

What was that?

MARY JANE. It's beginning to thunder and lightning out, Mr. Franklin!

RITCHIE. Lightning! That's just what I've been waiting for! Miss Mary Jane, get me my kite!

MARY JANE. Here it is, Mr. Franklin!

(*Footsteps, door opens, fade in terrific storm—wind, rain, and thunder*)

MINUTEMAN. I'll help you launch it, Mr. Franklin!

RITCHIE. Thank you, son! There she goes! Now! Hand me that key, Miss Mary Jane!

MARY JANE. Here you are, sir! (*Aside, hero-worshiping*) Oh,

I wonder what he's going to invent now!

RITCHIE. I think the kite's up high enough! Now, watch carefully, everyone! I'm going to touch this key to the kite string!

(*Sputter of electric arc. Cheat storm down a little to emphasize this*)

ALL (*"Ohhhs" and "Ahhhhhs"*).

RITCHIE (*dramatically*). Gentlemen! I have decided to call my invention—*electricity!!!!*

(*Sputter of arc up sharply*)

OUCH!!!!

(*Storm cuts out abruptly*)

MAC. Ritchie, I told yuh you'd get a shock if yuh touched that Square-D switch. After all the times I've let you play with that linotype, you oughta know better!

RITCHIE. Gosh! I burned my finger!—an' it hurts . . . !

MAC. Here . . . let me see it.

RITCHIE. Ow!

MAC. That's kind of a bad burn. We better go next door, an' I'll give yuh some first aid. (*Calling*) Joe! Lock up that editorial page, will you?

(*Music: Bridge . . . segue into "Inside a Kid's Head" theme*)

WOMAN. Guide, what's happening now? I can't see a thing!

GUIDE. Nothing's happening, ma'am. The boy's asleep—and he's not even dreaming.

MAN. How come?

GUIDE. I think he's blown a fuse in his imagination. Besides, he's had a pretty tough day. But something ought to be happening soon. You see, it's morning already.

MOTHER (*distant and muffled*). Ritchie! Ritchie! Wake up!

GUIDE (*fading*). That's his mother calling him now.

MOTHER (*on mike, clear*). Wake up, Ritchie!

(*Babble of voices in the background*)

RITCHIE (*waking up*). Huh? (*With a start*) Say! What's going on downstairs?

MOTHER. Put on your bathrobe and come down. Just about everybody in town's here! (*Fading*) Your father's so excited he can hardly talk.

RITCHIE (*half to himself*). Gee whiz! *Now* what have I done? (*Rustle of bedclothes*) Dawgone! This sleeve's always wrong side out!

(*Footsteps—slippers. Gallop downstairs. Babbling of crowd fades in*)

VOICE (*fading in*). Price, that's the cleverest political move that's ever been made in this state. You're as good as in office right now!

FATHER (*beaming*). Thank you! Thank you!

SECOND VOICE. That editorial of yours has blasted the state highway commission wide open!

WINKLER. What *I* can't understand, Price, is how you got the opposition paper to print that editorial of yours!

FATHER (*on thin ice*). Well . . . you're not the only one, J.D.! (*An uncertain little laugh*)

RITCHIE (*tugging at his mother's skirts*). Mom, what's happened?

MOTHER. Well, that article of your father's is in the morning paper.

RITCHIE (*fearing the worst*). Oh, gee! (*Suddenly*) Hey! What's Mary Jane doing here!?

MOTHER. She came over with her father. (*Distressed*) Oh, dear! I wish I'd put those new curtains up yesterday! Everybody in town's here to congratulate your father!

VOICE (*fading in*). A brilliant article, Price—brilliant! Frankly, though, I didn't quite get that reference in the last paragraph to the "Continental Congress."

FATHER (*self-conscious laugh*). Well, there are a *number* of people here who didn't understand that!

MOTHER (*fading in—low, confidential, to Father*). Ralph, I'm so proud of you. But how *did* that article get printed in the paper?

FATHER (*low*). Darned if I know. Somebody must've just taken it out of my pocket, and . . . (*Comes the dawn*) Sa-a-ay! (*Eyes narrowing*) Ritchie!

RITCHIE (*with a wholly futile front of innocence*). Yes, father?

FATHER (*slowly*). You didn't happen to take anything out of my pocket last night, did you?

RITCHIE (*groping*). As a matter of fact, I did. . . . (*Then blurting, fast*) But I jes' meant to get the note from Miss Ludlow, 'cause you were so upset! I got your article by mistake, an' I was gonna put it back! Honest I was!

FATHER. But how in blazes did it get in the paper?

RITCHIE (*very fast*). Well . . . I went down to see Mac . . . an' he let me play with the linotype machine . . . an' I guess I set up your speech . . . an' I guess Joe put it in the form . . . (*Trailing off, weakly*) an' I guess it got in the paper (*Pleading*) Please don't be mad!

FATHER. Mad! (*Expansive, full voice*) *Folks! I want you to meet my boy!!!*

RITCHIE (*nonplussed*). Gee whiz!

FATHER. If I'm elected on Tuesday . . .

VOICE (*off confidently*). You will be, Ralph!

FATHER. Well, then—all the credit goes to Ritchie here! If it weren't for what he did, I wouldn't stand a chance of being state assemblyman!

ALL (*babble of exclamation*).

MARY JANE (*fading in*). Oh, Ritchie! I'm so proud of you! (*Kisses him audibly*)

RITCHIE (*bubbling*). Gosh, Mary Jane! You kissed me! Gee whiz! You kissed me on the cheek!!!!

FATHER (*still expansive*). You know—I'd like to make a prediction right now! I'll bet dollars to doughnuts my boy Ritchie will be one of the great political leaders of his day!!!!

(*Music: Vibraphone—bong! As before—and Ritchie goes off into another dream*)

RITCHIE (*solemnly*). Gentlemen! I shall be very happy to speak at Gettysburg!

(*Music: Big curtain*)

TALKING ABOUT THE PLAY

1. This play is about Ritchie—a boy with a lively imagination. He loves to daydream exciting adventures whenever he gets bored with the real world around him. What kind of adventures does he daydream? What school subject seems to be the source of his daydreams? What do these daydreams tell you about Ritchie's personality?

2. The authors of the play thought it would be more fun to conduct the reader through Ritchie's brain while he daydreams, rather than just tell about the daydreams. What humor do you find in the scenes between the guide and the visitors? What parts of the brain did they notice? What unusual things happened in Ritchie's brain?

3. What is Miss Ludlow's attitude toward Ritchie? How would you describe her personality? What do you think

she wrote in the note to Ritchie's parents? How did this note help bring about a happy ending to the play?

4. What kind of people are Ritchie's parents? How would you feel if you were a parent and had a child who did the things that Ritchie did?

5. Mary Jane is an important person in all of Ritchie's daydreams. What did you learn about her in the daydreams and in the real-life scenes? Is she different in the daydreams than she is in real life? At the end of the play, what is Mary Jane's attitude toward Ritchie?

6. When and how does the voice of Mac appear again and again in Ritchie's daydreams? Suppose that Mac had not been a good friend of Ritchie's and had not let him use the linotype; or suppose that someone had checked the editorial page before the page was printed. What might have happened then to end the play?

7. This is a radio play, so the playwrights used sound effects to help show the action and to make the changes between scenes in the play. Which sound effects showed action? Which showed changes between the real world and the imaginary world? Each time Ritchie started to daydream, how did the sound effects give a signal to the tourists and the readers? Which sound effects helped you most to enjoy the play?

FOR YOUR OWN WRITING

1. Most people daydream at one time or another. You probably remember some marvelous daydreams you had in school, at home, or while doing your homework. Write about one of your daydreams, or make one up.

2. If you were the author of the play, what other places, times, people, and events in history might your main character dream about? Make a list of the historical events you would use.

DR. HEIDEGGER'S EXPERIMENT

NATHANIEL HAWTHORNE

dramatized by
Marvin G. Robinson

DR. HEIDEGGER'S EXPERIMENT

Can you imagine yourself, or your friends, as very old people? Can you imagine an older friend or relative as he must have been when he was young? What would happen if people could change their ages back and forth, as they wished, by magic?

Dr. Heidegger's Experiment shows five interesting people in a highly unusual situation. As you read this play, keep the characters clearly separate in your mind; don't get them mixed up. Try to discover the personality characteristics of each one, and try to guess what kind of person each one was when he was young.

Here, the story is presented as a stage dramatization. The *setting*—the place where the play happens—is Dr. Heidegger's study. As you read the play, try to picture the action in your mind as clearly as if you were seeing the play performed on a stage. Picture the old-fashioned costumes that the characters would be wearing. Imagine the expressions on their faces. Remember that the actors would look like old people. If you were playing one of the roles, what kind of face make-up might you use? How could your hair be fixed?

Whether you read this play silently or out loud (or even if your class acts it out), your imagination can make the scene complete. In your imagination, the costumes and scenery can be absolutely perfect—and they won't cost you a cent!

CHARACTERS

DR. HEIDEGGER, in his late sixties, a small-town doctor

MR. MEDBOURNE, in his sixties, a gambler at heart

COLONEL KILLIGREW, in his late sixties, still fond of women

MR. GASCOIGNE, about sixty-five, a former politician

WIDOW WYCHERLY, in her early seventies, once very beautiful

SCENE. *Dr. Heidegger's study, a dim, old-fashioned room*
(*When the curtain rises, the* WIDOW WYCHERLY *is seated in an armchair reading a magazine,* COLONEL KILLIGREW *and* MR. MEDBOURNE *are seated at a table opposite each other, and* MR. GASCOIGNE *glances at books in a bookcase right.*)

MR. MEDBOURNE (*looking at his watch*). It's four o'clock. We've waited half an hour already, and for what?

THE COLONEL (*puzzled*). I'm sure I don't know. What did your message say?

MR. MEDBOURNE. Simply to meet Dr. Heidegger in his study at half-past three; that it was important.

THE COLONEL. That's what mine said. I can't understand it at all. Mr. Gascoigne, do you know why we are here?

MR. GASCOIGNE (*absorbed in a book*). What's that?

THE COLONEL. Have you any idea why we are here?

MR. GASCOIGNE. None whatever! I merely followed instructions. Queer man, Dr. Heidegger. He's up to something, no doubt.

THE WIDOW (*laying aside her magazine*). Well, whatever it is, gentlemen, you may rest assured it'll be worth waiting for! I've known the doctor for more than fifty years. He's never disappointed me yet.

THE COLONEL. Tell me, Widow Wycherly, is there any truth in the rumors about the doctor? They say he is a magician and performs feats of magic.

THE WIDOW. Don't you believe it, my dear Colonel! The only magic Dr. Heidegger performs is strictly in connection with his medicine. Every doctor is somewhat of a magician, I believe.

MR. MEDBOURNE. I've heard tell he keeps a skeleton here.

THE WIDOW. I shouldn't wonder. It's quite customary.

MR. MEDBOURNE. It isn't Christian. Ashes to ashes, the good book says! What right has anyone to keep a body from its proper resting place?

MR. GASCOIGNE. Nonsense! As though it made a bit of difference where our bones are kept after we're gone. Anyway, you've only heard that the doctor keeps a skeleton here; you don't really know.

MR. MEDBOURNE. Don't I, though? Well, just look for yourself in that closet back there. (*He points to a cabinet near left.*)

MR. GASCOIGNE. I will!

(*He starts for the cabinet. As he reaches the rear of the table, the door to the anteroom opens, and* DR. HEIDEGGER *enters.*)

DR. HEIDEGGER. Good afternoon, gentlemen! (MR. GASCOIGNE *stops abruptly. The other men rise.*) And Widow Wycherly! You all received my message, I see. Good!

MR. MEDBOURNE. We've been waiting since half-past three, Doctor!

DR. HEIDEGGER. Oh, that's too bad! I thought we were to meet at four.

THE WIDOW. Why all the mystery, Doctor? What do you want of us?

DR. HEIDEGGER. Do sit down, gentlemen. I shall explain. (COLONEL KILLIGREW *and* MR. MEDBOURNE *return to their seats.* MR. GASCOIGNE *sits at the head of the table, between them.* DR. HEIDEGGER *crosses front.*) My dear old friends, I should like you to help me in one of my little experiments with which I amuse myself here in my study.

THE COLONEL. If it has anything to do with magic, I for one am not interested.

MR. MEDBOURNE. Nor I. I don't believe in meddling with God's secrets.

DR. HEIDEGGER. Forgive me if I fail to make myself plain. May I explain?

THE WIDOW. Please do, Doctor. Gentlemen, I'm sure Dr. Heidegger means no harm.

DR. HEIDEGGER. None whatever! Friends, I have known you for many, many years. We were children together. We grew old together. That is why I have chosen you four for my little experiment.

MR. GASCOIGNE. Pray tell us what experiment, Dr. Heidegger.

DR. HEIDEGGER. In due time! Colonel Killigrew, how many women have you loved in your lifetime?

THE COLONEL. I beg your pardon!

DR. HEIDEGGER. Let's be honest, Colonel. Is it not true that you have spent the best years of your life in pursuit of first one woman and then another?

THE COLONEL (*very much upset*). I refuse to to be humiliated publicly like this. Dr. Heidegger, how dare you, sir?

THE WIDOW. You know the doctor is right, Colonel. Why do you resent the truth? You even loved me in my youth. Why, you were my most ardent suitor at one time!

THE COLONEL. I've been a good man all my life, more or less.

I may have dabbled in love a little, but after all, I consider that my business.

DR. HEIDEGGER. Exactly, Colonel Killigrew, your business! Mr. Gascoigne, were you not at one time a politician?

MR. GASCOIGNE. I was.

DR. HEIDEGGER. As I recall, when a young man you enjoyed quite a reputation as a platform speaker. You were headed for big things, politically. What happened to that career?

MR. GASCOIGNE. I should prefer not to discuss my past, if you don't mind, Doctor.

DR. HEIDEGGER. But I do mind, my dear Mr. Gascoigne. Could it be true that you were discovered accepting bribes?

MR. GASCOIGNE. No one has any proof of that!

THE COLONEL. It's been common gossip for years.

MR. GASCOIGNE. I refuse to discuss it further.

DR. HEIDEGGER. Mr. Medbourne, your youth was an interesting one as I recall. At one time you had quite a fortune, Mr. Medbourne. Is this not so?

MR. MEDBOURNE. It is.

DR. HEIDEGGER. What happened to your money?

MR. MEDBOURNE. Well, if you must know, I invested it in stocks.

DR. HEIDEGGER. And lost?

MR. MEDBOURNE. Everything.

DR. HEIDEGGER. Then there is no truth in the rumor that you gambled heavily in night clubs?

MR. MEDBOURNE. None whatsoever!

THE WIDOW. Why, Mr. Medbourne, I recall going dancing with you myself when you lost hundreds playing cards.

DR. HEIDEGGER. Was our friend Mr. Medbourne an old suitor of yours, too?

THE WIDOW. Of course he was. And so was Charlie—Mr. Gascoigne.

DR. HEIDEGGER. You were very beautiful when you were young, my dear!

THE WIDOW. Was I?

DR. HEIDEGGER. Very! I loved you myself once.

THE WIDOW. Did you really?

DR. HEIDEGGER. I never told you though. You had so many beaux: Mr. Gascoigne, Mr. Medbourne, Colonel Killigrew.

THE COLONEL. I fail to see what all this has to do with any experiment.

DR. HEIDEGGER. Forgive me! (*He takes a faded rose from his coat pocket.*) Do you see this rose? This rose, this same withered and crumbling flower, blossomed over fifty years ago. It was given to me by Sylvia Ward, whose portrait hangs over there. I meant to wear it at our wedding. But Sylvia was killed the day before we were to be married. I have treasured this for fifty years. Now, would you believe it possible that this rose of half a century could ever bloom again?

THE WIDOW. Nonsense! You might as well ask if an old woman's wrinkled face could ever bloom again.

DR. HEIDEGGER. See for yourself! (*He uncovers the vase on the table and drops the rose into the water. When he takes it out, it is in full bloom.*) There, my friends, it looks as fresh as when Sylvia gave it to me.

MR. GASCOIGNE. That is certainly a clever trick. Pray tell us how you did it.

DR. HEIDEGGER. Did you never hear of the "Fountain of Youth" which Ponce de León, the Spanish adventurer, went in search of two or three centuries ago?

THE WIDOW. But did Ponce de León ever find it?

DR. HEIDEGGER. No, for he never sought it in the right place. The famous "Fountain of Youth," if I am rightly informed, is in the southern part of Florida, not far from the sea. Its source is overshadowed by several gigantic magnolias, which, though numberless centuries old, have been kept as fresh as violets by the virtues of this wonderful water. An acquaintance of mine, knowing my curiosity in scientific matters, has sent me this vaseful.

THE COLONEL. Ahem! And what may be the effect of this fluid on the human body?

DR. HEIDEGGER. You shall judge for yourself, my dear Colonel, and all of you, my respected friends, are welcome to so much of this admirable water as may restore to you the bloom of youth. For my own part, I am in no hurry to grow young again. With your permission, therefore, I will merely watch the progress of the experiment. (*He has filled four glasses with the water.*)

THE COLONEL. I'd be delighted to try it. So far as I'm concerned, I think the whole thing is nonsense.

MR. MEDBOURNE. So do I. Just a trick in magic.

MR. GASCOIGNE. Give me my glass. I may as well enjoy this joke with the rest of you.

DR. HEIDEGGER. Before you drink, my respectable old friends, it would be well that, with the experience of a lifetime to direct you, you should draw up a few general rules for your guidance in passing a second time through the perils of youth. Think what a sin and shame it would be if with your peculiar advantages you should not become patterns of virtue and wisdom to all the young people of the age! (*The four laugh.*) Drink, then! I rejoice that I have so well selected the subjects of my experiment.

(THE WIDOW *crosses to the table for her glass.* DR. HEIDEGGER *sits in the armchair. The four drink and place their glasses on the table. They begin to react to the water.*)

THE COLONEL. My! My!

MR. GASCOIGNE. I do believe—

THE WIDOW (*adjusting her hat*). We are younger. I feel younger. But we are still too old. Quick, let's drink some more of the water. May we, Doctor?

DR. HEIDEGGER. Of course—all you want. You have been a long time growing old. Surely, you might be content to grow young a little slower.

(*They fill their glasses again, snatch them up, and drink the water in a single gulp.*)

THE COLONEL. My dear Widow, you are charming! I've never seen you look more lovely.

THE WIDOW. You're making fun of me.

(*She runs to a mirror right and admires herself, fixing her hair.*)

MR. GASCOIGNE (*slightly intoxicated*). Gentlemen! Gentlemen! We are met on an occasion of great importance. This day of days shall be recorded in history. The constitution must be defended. I shall not fail in my duty which is dear to me. Down with tyranny! Down with communism! We are Americans and as Americans we will fight for that which is right. (*During the latter part of his speech, he has risen to great heights. He brings his fist down on the table and a moment later finds himself in his chair, a little bewildered. During this speech the* COLONEL *has been humming a tune and tapping on his glass.*)

THE COLONEL (*crossing behind the* WIDOW). Darling! I am overcome with your beauty.

MR. MEDBOURNE (*who has been counting his money visibly on the table*). Three, ten, twenty, twenty-five, fifty, sixty, seventy, seventy-five—four seventy-five! Now with any sort of odds I should double this. Then if I bet ten on Lightning to win—

THE WIDOW (*tripping lightly to the table*). My dear Charlie, pray favor me with another glass!

MR. GASCOIGNE. Certainly, my dear Madam, certainly! (*He begins pouring.*)

THE COLONEL. Allow me, my dear!

MR. GASCOIGNE. I have taken care of the lady.

(*Drinks are poured for them all. They drink at once.*)

THE WIDOW (*exultingly*). I am young! I am young again! Oh, look at my funny clothes! Ha, ha!

THE COLONEL. And look at me! (*He laughs.*) How could I ever wear such stuff?

MR. MEDBOURNE. The doctor, why he's got one foot in the grave already. The poor old man. Hooray, I am young!

THE COLONEL. Hooray!

MR. GASCOIGNE. Hooray!

(*They leap around the room and exercise gaily.*)

THE WIDOW (*tripping up to the doctor's chair*). Doctor, you dear old soul, get up and dance with me!

(*They all laugh loudly.*)

DR. HEIDEGGER (*quietly*). Pray excuse me. I am old and rheumatic, and my dancing days were over long ago. But any of these gay young gentlemen will be glad of so pretty a partner.

THE COLONEL. Dance with me, Clara!

MR. GASCOIGNE (*shouting*). No, no, I will be her partner!

MR. MEDBOURNE. She promised me her hand fifty years ago!

(*They all gather round her. One catches her hands and the other two throw their arms around her waist. They struggle and laugh. THE WIDOW dodges from one to the other. The men begin to get mad and struggle with each other. Finally they bang into the table upsetting the vase of water.*)

DR. HEIDEGGER. Come, come, gentlemen—come, Madam Wycherly. You must stop this riot. (*He motions them to be seated. They obey.*) My poor Sylvia's rose! It appears to be fading again. (*The four shiver a little.*) Still I love it as well thus as in its dewy freshness.

THE COLONEL. My youth—it is going—I am getting old again.

MR. GASCOIGNE. What is happening? I have changed.

THE WIDOW. Are we—are we grown old again, so soon? (*She cries with her hands before her face.*)

DR. HEIDEGGER. Yes, friends, you are old again. And lo! the water of youth is all spilled over the floor. Well, I do not care, for if the fountain gushed at my very doorstep, I would not stoop to bathe my lips in it—no, not if I could be young for years instead of minutes. Such is the lesson you have taught me!

(*Curtain*)

TALKING ABOUT THE PLAY

1. At the beginning of the play, how does each guest feel toward Dr. Heidegger and toward his message? What do their statements and actions reveal about each of their personalities?

2. Soon after greeting his old friends, Dr. Heidegger tells them all about their faults. Why does he do this to his guests? How do these details help you understand the characters of these people?

3. When Dr. Heidegger shows them the rose and describes his experiment, how do the guests react? Is this the way they might be expected to react? How might different people have reacted? Why does the Doctor think he has selected the right people for his experiment? Do you agree with him?

4. How do the people act as they go through the experiment? Do you think they learned anything from the experiment? What else do you think they could have learned from the experiment?

5. What is the Doctor trying to find out in his experiment? Why do people want to be young? How might other people behave if they could become young again, or if they could stay young forever? Why do you suppose the Doctor prefers to watch the experiment and not take part in it?

6. Is the end of the play a surprise, or not? Had the playwright given you any clues to the ending? How else might the playwright have ended the play?

7. How is the rose like the people? How does the rose help show the playwright's ideas? Can you sum up the main idea or theme of the play?

8. Do you think the people actually became young again, or did they just *think* they were young? Was the Doctor really a magician? Does the play give you a single clear answer to this question?

FOR YOUR OWN WRITING

1. Experiments in magic have always fascinated people. Imagine you have just conducted an experiment in magic in your secret laboratory. Write a report describing the experiment and the result.

2. Suppose there were a potion that could make you suddenly grown-up or younger. What age would you like to be? Why? Explain your ideas in an essay.

3. Ponce de León searched a lifetime for the Fountain of Youth. Go back in history and pretend you are traveling with Ponce de León. One day you discover the Fountain of Youth. Write a story or a letter, telling about the marvelous discovery and the events that follow.

GRANDPA AND THE STATUE

ARTHUR MILLER

GRANDPA AND THE STATUE

Can you think of an important statue or public monument? Why is it important? What does it remind you of? What does it stand for?

In *Grandpa and the Statue*, the playwright shows people with different attitudes toward the Statue of Liberty. One person's attitude even changes during the action of the play.

To tell his story, the playwright uses a special technique called the *flashback*. As a character remembers the past, the playwright takes you along in the character's thoughts, and you see the very scenes and events that the character remembers. Thus the plot "flashes back" in time, to show you what happened in earlier years.

As you read this play, watch carefully for the flashbacks. Some scenes take place in the present time of the play, and other scenes are young Monaghan's memories of the past. As you follow the action of the play back and forth in time, you will also need to identify the different characters called "Monaghan." In the present, we meet a soldier called "Monaghan," or "Young Monaghan." In the past, we see this same man as a child, "Child Monaghan." In the past, too, we meet his grandfather, called simply "Monaghan."

Grandpa and the Statue is a radio play. The playwright has used sound effects and special signals. Music, for instance, indicates flashbacks and other changes of time and place.

CHARACTERS

Characters in the present time of the play:

ANNOUNCER

AUGUST

MONAGHAN (Young Monaghan, a soldier)

Characters from the past, heard in the flashback scenes which Young Monaghan remembers:

SHEEAN

MONAGHAN (Grandfather of Young Monaghan)

CHILD MONAGHAN (Young Monaghan himself, as a child)

GEORGE

CHARLEY

JACK   (neighborhood children, Child Monaghan's friends)

MIKE

JOE

ALF

GIRL   (passengers on the Statue of Liberty boat)

YOUNG MAN

MEGAPHONE VOICE

VETERAN (visitor to the Statue)

(*Music: Theme*)

ANNOUNCER. The scene is the fourth floor of a giant army hospital overlooking New York Harbor. A young man sitting in a wheel chair is looking out a window—just looking. After a while another young man in another wheel chair rolls over to him and they both look.

(*Music out*)

AUGUST. You want to play some checkers with me, Monaghan?

MONAGHAN. Not right now.

AUGUST. Okay. (*Slight pause*) You don't want to go feeling blue, Monaghan.

MONAGHAN. I'm not blue.

AUGUST. All you do most days is sit here looking out this window.

MONAGHAN. What do you want me to do, jump rope?

AUGUST. No, but what do you get out of it?

MONAGHAN. It's a beautiful view. Some companies make millions of dollars just printing that view on postcards.

AUGUST. Yeh, but nobody keeps looking at a postcard six, seven hours a day.

MONAGHAN. I come from around here, it reminds me of things. My young days.

AUGUST. That's right, you're Brooklyn, aren't you?

MONAGHAN. My house is only about a mile away.

AUGUST. That so. Tell me, are you looking at just the water all the time? I'm curious. I don't get a kick out of this view.

MONAGHAN. There's the Statue of Liberty out there. Don't you see it?

AUGUST. Oh, that's it. Yeh, that's nice to look at.

MONAGHAN. I like it. Reminds me of a lot of laughs.

AUGUST. Laughs? The Statue of Liberty?

MONAGHAN. Yeh, my grandfather. He got all twisted up with the Statue of Liberty.

AUGUST (*laughs a little*). That so? What happened?

MONAGHAN. Well. My grandfather was the stingiest man in Brooklyn. "Mercyless" Monaghan, they used to call him. He even used to save umbrella handles.

AUGUST. What for?

MONAGHAN. Just couldn't stand seeing anything go to waste. After a big windstorm there'd be a lot of broken umbrellas laying around in the streets.

AUGUST. Yeh?

MONAGHAN. He'd go around picking them up. In our house the closets were always full of umbrella handles. My grandma used to say that he would go across the Brooklyn Bridge on the trolley just because he could come back on the same nickel. See, if you stayed on the trolley they'd let you come back for the same nickel.

AUGUST. What'd he do, just go over and come back?

MONAGHAN. Yeh, it made him feel good. Savin' money. Two and a half cents.

AUGUST. So how'd he get twisted up with the Statue of Liberty?

MONAGHAN. Well, way back in 1887 around there they were living on Butler Street. Butler Street, Brooklyn, practically runs right down to the river. One day he's sitting on the front porch, reading a paper he borrowed from the neighbors, when along comes this man Jack Sheean who lived up the block.

(*Music: Sneak into above speech, then bridge, then out*)

SHEEAN (*slight brogue*). A good afternoon to you, Monaghan.

MONAGHAN (*grandfather*). How're you, Sheean, how're ya?

SHEEAN. Fair, fair. And how's Mrs. Monaghan these days?

MONAGHAN. Warm. Same as everybody else in summer.

SHEEAN. I've come to talk to you about the fund, Monaghan.

MONAGHAN. What fund is that?

SHEEAN. The Statue of Liberty fund.

MONAGHAN. Oh, that.

SHEEAN. It's time we come to grips with the subject, Monaghan.

MONAGHAN. I'm not interested, Sheean.

SHEEAN. Now hold up on that a minute. Let me tell you the facts. This here Frenchman has gone and built a fine statue of Liberty. It costs the Lord knows how many millions to build. All they're askin' us to do is contribute enough to put up a base for the statue to stand on.

MONAGHAN. I'm not . . . !

SHEEAN. Before you answer me. People all over the whole United States are puttin' in for it. Butler Street is doin' the same. We'd like to hang up a flag on the corner saying

—"Butler Street, Brooklyn, is one hundred per cent behind the Statue of Liberty." And Butler Street *is* a hundred per cent subscribed except for you. Now will you give us a dime, Monaghan? One dime and we can put up the flag. Now what do you say to that?

MONAGHAN. I'm not throwin' me good money away for somethin' I don't even know exists.

SHEEAN. Now what do you mean by that?

MONAGHAN. Have you seen this statue?

SHEEAN. No, but it's in a warehouse. And as soon as we get the money to build the pedestal they'll take it and put it up on that island in the river, and all the boats comin' in from the old country will see it there and it'll raise the hearts of the poor immigrants to see such a fine sight on their first look at this country.

MONAGHAN. And how do I know it's in this here warehouse at all?

SHEEAN. You read your paper, don't you? It's been in all the papers for the past year.

MONAGHAN. Ha, the papers! Last year I read in the paper that they were about to pave Butler Street and take out all the holes. Turn around and look at Butler Street, Mr. Sheean.

SHEEAN. All right. I'll do this: I'll take you to the warehouse and show you the statue. Will you give me a dime then?

MONAGHAN. Well . . . I'm not sayin' I would, and I'm not sayin' I wouldn't. But I'd be more *likely* if I saw the thing large as life, I would.

SHEEAN (*peeved*). All right, then. Come along.

(*Music up and down and out*)

(*Footsteps, in a warehouse . . . echo . . . they come to a halt*)

Now then. Do you see the Statue of Liberty or don't you see it?

MONAGHAN. I see it all right, but it's all broke!

SHEEAN. *Broke!* They brought it from France on a boat. They had to take it apart, didn't they?

MONAGHAN. You got a secondhand statue, that's what you got, and I'm not payin' for new when they've shipped us something that's all smashed to pieces.

SHEEAN. Now just a minute, just a minute. Visualize what I'm about to tell you, Monaghan, get the picture of it. When this statue is put together it's going to stand ten stories high. Could they get a thing ten stories high into a four-story building such as this is? Use your good sense, now Monaghan.

MONAGHAN. What's that over there?

SHEEAN. Where?

MONAGHAN. That tablet there in her hand. What's it say? July Eye Vee (IV) MDCCLXXVI . . . what . . . what's all that?

SHEEAN. That means July 4, 1776. It's in Roman numbers. Very high class.

MONAGHAN. What's the good of it? If they're going to put a sign on her they ought to put it: Welcome All. That's it. Welcome All.

SHEEAN. They decided July 4, 1776, and July 4, 1776, it's going to be!

MONAGHAN. All right, then let them get their dime from somebody else!

SHEEAN. Monaghan!

MONAGHAN. No, sir! I'll tell you something. I didn't think there was a statue but there is. She's all broke, it's true, but she's here and maybe they can get her together. But even if they do, will you tell me what sort of a welcome to immigrants it'll be, to have a gigantic thing like that in the middle of the river and in her hand is July Eye Vee MCDVC . . . whatever it is?

SHEEAN. That's the date the country was made!

MONAGHAN. The divil with the date! A man comin' in from the sea wants a place to stay, not a date. When I come from the old country I git off at the dock and there's a feller says to me, "Would you care for a room for the night?" "I would that," I sez, and he sez, "All right then, follow me." He takes me to a rooming house. I no sooner sign me name on the register—which I was able to do even at that time— when I look around and the feller is gone clear away and took my valise in the bargain. A statue anyway can't move off so fast, but if she's going to welcome let her say welcome, not this MCDC. . . .

SHEEAN. All right, then, Monaghan. But all I can say is, you've laid a disgrace on the name of Butler Street. I'll put the dime in for ya.

MONAGHAN. Don't connect me with it! It's a swindle, is all it is. In the first place, it's broke; in the second place, if they do put it up it'll come down with the first high wind that strikes it.

SHEEAN. The engineers say it'll last forever!

MONAGHAN. And I say it'll topple into the river in a high wind! Look at the inside of her. She's all hollow!

SHEEAN. I've heard everything now, Monaghan. Just about everything. Good-bye.

MONAGHAN. What do you mean, good-bye? How am I to get back to Butler Street from here?

SHEEAN. You've got legs to walk.

MONAGHAN. I'll remind you that I come on the trolley.

SHEEAN. And I'll remind you that I paid your fare and I'm not repeating the kindness.

MONAGHAN. Sheean? You've stranded me!

(*Music up and down*)

YOUNG MONAGHAN. That was grandpa. That's why I have to laugh every time I look at the statue now.

AUGUST. Did he ever put the dime in?

YOUNG MONAGHAN. Well—in a way. What happened was this: His daughters got married and finally my mom . . . put *me* out on Butler Street. I got to be pretty attached to grandpa. He'd even give me an umbrella handle and make a sword out of it for me. Naturally, I wasn't very old before he began working on me about the statue.

(*High wind*)

CHILD MONAGHAN (*softly, as though grandpa is in bed*). Grampa?

MONAGHAN (*awakened*). Heh? What are you doin' up?

CHILD MONAGHAN. Ssssh! Listen!

(*Wind rising up and fading. Rising higher and fading*)

MONAGHAN (*gleefully*). Aaaaaaaah! Yes, yes. This'll do it, boy. This'll do it! First thing in the morning we'll go down to the docks and I'll bet you me life that Mr. Sheean's statue is smashed down and layin' on the bottom of the bay. Go to sleep now, we'll have a look first thing.

(*Music up and down*)

(*Footsteps*)

CHILD MONAGHAN. If it fell down, all the people will get their dimes back, won't they, grampa? Slow down, I can't walk so fast.

MONAGHAN. Not only will they get their dimes back, but Mr. Sheean and the whole crew that engineered the collection are going to rot in jail. Now mark my words. Here, now, we'll take a short cut around this shed . . .

(*Footsteps continue a moment, then gradually . . . disappointedly they come to a halt*)

CHILD MONAGHAN. She's . . . she's still standing, grampa.

MONAGHAN. She is that. (*Uncomprehending*) I don't understand it. That was a terrible wind last night. Terrible.

CHILD MONAGHAN. Maybe she's weaker though. Heh?

MONAGHAN. Why . . . sure, that must be it. I'll wager she's hangin' by a thread. (*Realizing*) Of course! That's why they put her out there in the water so when she falls down she won't be flattening out a lot of poor innocent people. Hey—feel that?

CHILD MONAGHAN. The wind! It's starting to blow again!

MONAGHAN. Sure, and look at the sky blackening over!

(*Wind rising*)

Feel it comin' up! Take your last look at the statue, boy. If I don't mistake me eyes she's takin' a small list to Jersey already!

(*Music up and down*)

YOUNG MONAGHAN. It was getting embarrassing for me on the block. I kept promising the other kids that when the next wind came the statue would come down. We even had a game. Four or five kids would stand in a semicircle around one kid who was the statue. The statue kid had to stand on his heels and look right in our eyes. Then we'd all take a deep breath and blow in his face. He'd fall down like a stick of wood. They all believed me and grampa . . . until one day. We were standing around throwing rocks at an old milk can . . .

(*Banging of rocks against milk can*)

GEORGE (*kid*). What're you doin'?

CHILD MONAGHAN. What do we look like we're doin'?

GEORGE. I'm going someplace tomorrow.

CHARLEY (*kid*). I know, church. Watch out, I'm throwin'.
(*Can being hit*)

GEORGE. I mean after church.

JACK. Where?

GEORGE. My old man's going to take me out on the Statue of Liberty boat.
(*Banging against can abruptly stops*)

CHILD MONAGHAN. You're not going out on the statue, though, are you?

GEORGE. Sure, that's where we're going.

CHILD MONAGHAN. But you're liable to get killed. Supposing there's a high wind tomorrow?

GEORGE. My old man says that statue couldn't fall down if all the wind in the world and John L. Sullivan hit it at the same time.

CHILD MONAGHAN. Is that so?

GEORGE. Yeh, that's so. My old man says that the only reason your grandfather's saying that it's going to fall down is that he's ashamed he didn't put a dime in for the pedestal.

CHILD MONAGHAN. Is that so?

GEORGE. Yeh, that's so.

CHILD MONAGHAN. Well, you tell your old man that if he gets killed tomorrow not to come around to my grandfather and say he didn't warn him!

JACK. Hey, George, would your father take me along?

GEORGE. I'll ask him, maybe he—

CHILD MONAGHAN. What, are you crazy, Jack?

MIKE. Ask him if he'd take me too, will ya, George?

CHILD MONAGHAN. Mike, what's the matter with you?

JOE. Me too, George, I'll ask my mother for money.

CHILD MONAGHAN. Joe! Didn't you hear what my grampa said?

JOE. Well . . . I don't really believe that any more.

CHILD MONAGHAN. You don't be . . .

MIKE. Me neither.

JACK. I don't really think your grampa knows what he's talkin' about.

CHILD MONAGHAN. He don't, heh? (*Ready to weep*) Okay . . . Okay. (*Bursting out*) I just hope that wind blows tomorrow, boy! I just hope that wind blows!

(*Music up and down*)

(*Creaking of a rocking chair*)

Grampa . . . ?

MONAGHAN. Huh?

CHILD MONAGHAN. Can you stop rocking for a minute?

(*Rocking stops*)

Can you put down your paper?

(*Rustle of paper*)

I—I read the weather report for tomorrow.

MONAGHAN. The weather report . . .

CHILD MONAGHAN. Yeh. It says fair and cool.

MONAGHAN. What of it?

CHILD MONAGHAN. I was wondering. Supposing you and me we went on a boat tomorrow. You know, I see the water every day when I go down to the docks to play, but I never sat on it. I mean in a boat.

MONAGHAN. Oh. Well, we might take the ferry on the Jersey side. We might do that.

CHILD MONAGHAN. Yeh, but there's nothing to see in Jersey.

MONAGHAN. You can't go to Europe tomorrow.

CHILD MONAGHAN. No, but couldn't we go toward the ocean? Just . . . *toward* it?

MONAGHAN. Toward it. What—what is it on your mind, boy? What is it now?

CHILD MONAGHAN. Well, I . . .

MONAGHAN. Oh, you want to take the Staten Island ferry. Sure, that's in the direction of the sea.

CHILD MONAGHAN. No, grampa, not the Staten Island ferry.

MONAGHAN. You don't mean—(*Breaks off*) Boy!

CHILD MONAGHAN. All the kids are going tomorrow with Georgie's old man.

MONAGHAN. You don't believe me any more.

CHILD MONAGHAN. I do, grampa, but . . .

MONAGHAN. You don't. If you did you'd stay clear of the Statue of Liberty for love of your life!

CHILD MONAGHAN. But, grampa, when is it going to fall down? All I do is wait and wait.

MONAGHAN (*with some uncertainty*). You've got to have faith.

CHILD MONAGHAN. But every kid in my class went to see it and now the ones that didn't are going tomorrow. And they all keep talking about it and all I do . . . Well, I can't keep telling them it's a swindle. I—I wish we could see it, grampa. It don't cost so much to go.

MONAGHAN. As long as you put it that way I'll have to admit I'm a bit curious meself as to how it's managed to stand upright so long. Tell you what I'll do. Barrin' wind, we'll chance it tomorrow!

CHILD MONAGHAN. Oh, gramp!

MONAGHAN. But! if anyone should ask you where we went you'll say—Staten Island. Are y' on?

CHILD MONAGHAN. Okay, sure. Staten Island.

MONAGHAN (*secretively*). We'll take the early boat, then. Mum's the word, now. For if old man Sheean hears that I went out there I'll have no peace from the thief the rest of m' life.

(*Music up and down*)

(*Boat whistles*)

CHILD MONAGHAN. Gee, it's nice ridin' on a boat, ain't it, grampa?

MONAGHAN. Never said there was anything wrong with the boat. Boat's all right. You're sure now that Georgie's father is takin' the kids in the afternoon.

CHILD MONAGHAN. Yeh, that's when they're going. Gee, look at those two sea gulls. Wee!—look at them swoop! They caught a fish!

MONAGHAN. What I can't understand is what all these people see in that statue that they'll keep a boat like this full makin' the trip, year in year out. To hear the newspapers talk, if the statue was gone we'd be at war with the nation that stole her the followin' mornin' early. All it is is a big high pile of French copper.

CHILD MONAGHAN. The teacher says it shows us that we got liberty.

MONAGHAN. Bah! If you've got liberty you don't need a statue to tell you you got it; and if you haven't got liberty no statue's going to do you any good tellin' you you got it. It was a criminal waste of the people's money. (*Quietly*) And just to prove it to you I'll ask this feller sitting right over there what he sees in it. You'll see what a madness the whole thing was. Say, mister?

ALF. Hey?

MONAGHAN. I beg your pardon. I'm a little strange here, and curious. Could you tell me why you're going to the Statue of Liberty?

ALF. Me? Well, I tell ya. I always wanted to take an ocean voyage. This is a pretty big boat—bigger than the ferries— so on Sundays, sometimes, I take the trip. It's better than nothing.

MONAGHAN. Thank you. (*To the kid*) So much for the great meaning of that statue, me boy. We'll talk to this lady standing at the rail. I just want you to understand why I didn't give Sheean me dime. Madam, would you be good enough to . . . Oh pardon me. (*To kid*) Better pass her by, she don't look so good. We'll ask that girl there. Young lady, if you'll pardon the curiosity of an old man . . . could you tell me in a few good words what it is about that statue that brings you out here?

GIRL. What statue?

MONAGHAN. Why, the Statue of Liberty up 'head. We're coming up to it.

GIRL. Statue of Liberty! Is this the Statue of Liberty boat?

MONAGHAN. Well, what'd you think it was?

GIRL. Oh, my! I'm supposed to be on the Staten Island ferry! Where's the ticket man? (*Going away*) Ticket man! Where's the ticket man?

CHILD MONAGHAN. Gee whiz, nobody seems to want to see the statue.

MONAGHAN. Just to prove it, let's see this fellow sitting on this bench here. Young man, say . . .

YOUNG MAN. I can tell you in one word. For four days I haven't had a minute's peace. My kids are screaming, my wife is yelling, upstairs they play the piano all day long. The only place I can find that's quiet is a statue. That statue is my sweetheart. Every Sunday I beat it out to the island and sit next to her, and she don't talk.

CHILD MONAGHAN. I guess you were right, grampa. Nobody seems to think it means anything.

MONAGHAN. Not only doesn't mean anything, but if they'd used the money to build an honest roomin' house on that island, the immigrants would have a place to spend the night, their valises wouldn't get robbed, and they—

MEGAPHONE VOICE. *Please keep your seats while the boat is docking. Statue of Liberty—all out in five minutes!*

CHILD MONAGHAN. Look down there, gramp! There's a peanut stand! Could I have some?

MONAGHAN. I feel the wind comin' up. I don't think we dare take the time.

(*Music up and down*)

CHILD MONAGHAN. Sssssseuuuuuww! Look how far you can see! Look at that ship way out in the ocean!

MONAGHAN. It is, it's quite a view. Don't let go of me hand now.

CHILD MONAGHAN. I betcha we could almost see California.

MONAGHAN. It's probably that grove of trees way out over there. They do say it's beyond Jersey.

CHILD MONAGHAN. Feels funny. We're standing right inside her head. Is that what you meant . . . July IV, MCD . . . ?

MONAGHAN. That's it. That tablet in her hand. Now shouldn't they have put Welcome All on it instead of that foreign language? Say! Do you feel her rockin'?

CHILD MONAGHAN. Yeah, she's moving a little bit. Listen, the wind!

(*Whistling of wind*)

MONAGHAN. We better get down, come on! This way!

CHILD MONAGHAN. No, the stairs are this way! Come on!

(*Running in echo. Then quick stop*)

MONAGHAN. No, I told you they're the other way! Come!

VETERAN (*calm, quiet voice*). Don't get excited, pop. She'll stand.

MONAGHAN. She's swayin' awful.

VETERAN. That's all right. I been up here thirty, forty times. She gives with the wind, flexible. Enjoy the view, go on.

MONAGHAN. Did you say you've been up here forty times?

VETERAN. About that many.

MONAGHAN. What do you find here that's so interesting?

VETERAN. It calms my nerves.

MONAGHAN. Ah. It seems to me it would make you more nervous than you were.

VETERAN. No, not me. It kinda means something to me.

MONAGHAN. Might I ask what?

VETERAN. Well . . . I was in the Philippine War . . . back in '98. Left my brother back there.

MONAGHAN. Oh, yes. Sorry I am to hear it. Young man, I suppose, eh?

VETERAN. Yeh. We were both young. This is his birthday today.

MONAGHAN. Oh, I understand.

VETERAN. Yeh, this statue is about the only stone he's got. In my mind I feel it is anyway. This statue kinda looks like what we believe. You know what I mean?

MONAGHAN. Looks like what we believe . . . I . . . I never thought of it that way. I . . . I see what you mean. It does look that way. (*Angrily*) See now, boy? If Sheean had put it that way I'd a give him me dime. (*Hurt*) Now, why do you suppose he didn't tell me that! Come down now. I'm sorry, sir, we've got to get out of here.

(*Music up and down*)

(*Footsteps under*)

Hurry now, I want to get out of here. I feel terrible. I do, boy. That Sheean, that fool. Why didn't he tell me that? You'd think . . .

CHILD MONAGHAN. What does this say?

(*Footsteps halt*)

MONAGHAN. Why, it's just a tablet, I suppose. I'll try it with me spectacles, just a minute. Why, it's a poem, I believe . . . "Give me your tired, your poor, your huddled masses yearning to breathe free, the wretched refuse of your teeming shore. Send these, the homeless, tempest-tost to me, I lift . . . my lamp beside . . . the golden door!" Oh, dear. (*Ready to weep*) It had Welcome All on it all the time. Why didn't Sheean tell me? I'd a given him a quarter! Boy . . . go over there and here's a nickel and buy yourself a bag of them peanuts.

CHILD MONAGHAN (*astonished*). Gramp!

MONAGHAN. Go on now, I want to study this a minute. And be sure the man gives you full count.

CHILD MONAGHAN. I'll be right back.

(*Footsteps running away*)

MONAGHAN (*to himself*). "Give me your tired, your poor, your huddled masses . . ."

(*Music swells from a sneak to full, then under to background*)

YOUNG MONAGHAN (*soldier*). I ran over and got my peanuts and stood there cracking them open, looking around. And I happened to glance over to grampa. He had his nose right up to that bronze tablet, reading it. And then he reached into his pocket and kinda spied around over his eyeglasses to see if anybody was looking, and then he took out a coin and stuck it in a crack of cement over the tablet. (*Coin falling onto concrete*)

It fell out and before he could pick it up I got a look at it. It was a half a buck. He picked it up and pressed it into the crack so it stuck. And then he came over to me and we went home.

(*Music: Change to stronger, more forceful theme*)

That's why, when I look at her now through this window,

I remember that time and that poem, and she really seems to say, Whoever you are, wherever you come from, Welcome All. Welcome Home.

(*Music: Flare up to finish*)

TALKING ABOUT THE PLAY

1. Do you think Grandpa's first attitude toward the Statue of Liberty indicates that he is an unpatriotic person? What other reasons may have made him refuse to contribute money? Can you think of any justification for Grandpa's concern over his money? What act by Grandpa helped show his true and final feeling for the Statue?
2. What two things seemed to have the strongest effect in changing Grandpa's attitude toward the Statue?
3. Why does the child Monaghan want to see the Statue? Does he lack faith in Grandpa? What influence do the other children have on him?
4. The playwright brings out some important ideas as Grandpa questions the different visitors to the Statue. All the people questioned give reasons for their visits. Who gives the best reason? What idea or theme of the play is the author stating through the words of the people questioned?
5. As Monaghan begins to tell August about Grandpa, the play moves back to Monaghan's childhood. This technique of going back in time is called the *flashback*. How else might the playwright have shown the same actions and ideas effectively without using flashbacks?
6. As the play begins, we find Monaghan in an army hospital. Why is he there? How does the location of the room Monaghan is in affect his thoughts?

FOR YOUR OWN WRITING

1. The words carved on the statue, "Give me your tired, your poor . . ." are part of a poem by Emma Lazarus. Look up the complete poem. Write an essay telling about your response to the poem.

2. The episodes in this play are told as Monaghan remembers them. Do you think the story might be different if Grandpa were telling it? Write one or more of the episodes as Grandpa might tell them. You may use some of the dialogue from the play, if you wish.

3. Describe a visit to the Statue of Liberty, as told by the veteran in the play, by one of the other visitors that Grandpa questioned, or by yourself if you visited the Statue.

4. In every city, town, or village there are historical monuments or statues. Think about one near your home or school. Write an interesting story about a visit to the monument or statue.

ATTUCKS,
THE MARTYR

ATTUCKS, THE MARTYR

What qualities must a patriotic person have? What makes an individual risk his own safety for the sake of a cause?

In *Attucks, the Martyr*, these questions will be considered. You will see a true episode taken from the early history of America. The colonists had many grievances against England at this time but no method of recourse. Crispus Attucks, a former slave, felt intensely about the injustice of the British and tried to do something about it.

As you read the play, observe the feelings that people have toward Attucks. Also notice what kind of things Attucks himself says. What people say about Attucks and what Attucks himself says will tell you quite a bit about his character.

Attucks, the Martyr is a play filled with strong emotions. You will become involved in the clash of individual personalities, as well as the clash of political ideals. The characters, in playing out their roles, clearly show where they stand in relation to this clash.

As you read the play, imagine that you are back in revolutionary times. Examine the motives of the characters, and see if you can also take sides.

CHARACTERS

CRISPUS ATTUCKS, a Negro patriot.

CALDWELL

GRAY ⎫ his companions.

MAVERICK

MR. STEELE, a rich Tory.

MR. CARR, a tobacconist.

MAJOR EVERING, a British officer.

Crispus Attucks is the only Negro character in this play.
All the costumes are those of the Revolutionary period.

(*Place: Boston*)

(*Time: March 5, 1770*)

(*We see a barely furnished room on the second floor of a building facing what is now* STATE STREET. *At the right is a door which leads to the stairway, and below this door stands a chair against the wall. At the rear is a wide window and against the left wall is a large wardrobe. Just above the center of the floor is a rectangular table of unpolished wood, above and to the right of which are chairs. A gun is leaning in the upper right corner. When we first see the room* MR. CARR *is standing at the left of the window watching a scene in the* street below. *Suddenly* MR. CARR *looks more closely as if he sees someone entering the store below; then he goes to the door and opens it, calling downstairs.*)

CARR (*holding the door open*). Come right up, Mr. Steele! (*He then waits until his visitor enters. The man who appears is the wealthy* MR. STEELE, *whose three-cornered hat and other clothing are all more fashionable and expensive than anything* MR. CARR *wears.*) I've been expecting you all morning.

STEELE. Yes, I thought you would be.

CARR (*offering his visitor a chair at the right of the table*). Won't you sit down?

STEELE (*sitting at the right and resting his richly-carved walking stick on the table*). Thank you.

CARR (*standing at the table*). I suppose things are quiet in your part of town.

STEELE. It is unfortunate that things are not quiet in all parts. These would-be rebels are trying to make trouble for the king's soldiers. (CARR *is silent and* STEELE *looks up at him inquiringly before speaking.*)

STEELE. I suppose it's not necessary for me to ask you, Mr. Carr, if you are still on the side of King George III.

CARR. No, that's not necessary, Mr. Steele. I am still loyal to our sovereign.

STEELE (*after observing the whole room in a casual manner*). That's certainly good to hear in these rebellious times. And now a word of advice. (CARR *sits attentively.*) Although I know you are a loyal subject, it may not be known to everyone.

CARR. I never attempt to hide it, sir.

STEELE. I know that. But a stranger coming here—a soldier, let us say—might think otherwise if he saw your gun in the corner. (*He motions towards the gun.*)

CARR (*rising*). I'll put it away at once. (*He takes the gun from the corner and puts it into the wardrobe.*)

STEELE. That, I think, is much better, even if it is unloaded.

CARR. It is loaded; but not against any loyal friend of the king.

STEELE. Well said if you mean that you would never use it against the king's friends, but against his enemies.

CARR (*sitting again*). That is exactly what I mean.

STEELE. Good. Then I can inform you that the loan of one hundred pounds mentioned between us will be delivered to you this evening.

CARR. I thank you for your kindness, but I must add that the hope of getting the loan has not influenced my opinions in anyway. I believe as I have always believed.

STEELE (*rising and pacing the floor*). I like your frankness, Mr. Carr; and for that reason I am going to mention another subject that in a way concerns you.

CARR (*interested*). What is that, Mr. Steele?

STEELE (*stopping*). You know a man—a black man—named Crispus Attucks?

CARR (*rising*). Yes, I know him. What about him?

STEELE. Did you know that for years he has been a fugitive slave, and there is a reward on his head?

CARR. I did not.

STEELE. I have found out that years ago he was owned by someone who is still offering ten pounds for his capture.

CARR (*with great interest*). Really?

STEELE (*pacing again*). I have seen this man, Attucks. He is one of the boldest rebels; and besides, he has some intelligence, which makes him more dangerous.

CARR. He comes here from time to time.

STEELE. Yes, I know he does. He and his friends are all enemies of King George.

CARR. I admit they talk in a rebellious manner, but I let them continue to meet here because they are good customers of mine.

STEELE. The British soldiers will begin looking for him today. Nothing would please the British officers more than to see Crispus Attucks captured and sent back to his master. Anyone fearless and inclined to leadership as he is, is dangerous to our cause.

CARR. Even if he's bold, he shouldn't be hard to capture.

STEELE. Someone who can use a little pocket money will capture him. (*Stopping suddenly.*) Does he go armed?

CARR. I don't think so.

STEELE (*relieved*). That much is in our favor. (*A cheer is heard outside.*)

CARR (*turning and looking out of the window*). There seems to be a larger crowd in the street today.

STEELE. Yes, every day the rabble becomes bolder. They crowd the streets, hurl insults at His Majesty's troops, and do everything else they can to bring the situation to the breaking point.

CARR. I hope there'll be no serious trouble.

STEELE. Well, soldiers are soldiers, and some of them are just as hot-tempered as the members of this mob.

CARR. I know. That's where the danger lies.

STEELE. The soldiers haven't disturbed you as yet, have they?

CARR. No.

STEELE. I hope they don't.

CARR. I have no fear of trouble.

STEELE. Good. I'm glad to see you so confident, Mr. Carr. (*He takes his stick from the table.*) I must be going now. I have another stop to make in your neighborhood, and on my way back I'll stop in for my weekly supply of tobacco and give you the loan I promised.

CARR. Thank you. I enjoyed our talk, Mr. Steele.

STEELE. I always enjoy talking to His Majesty's loyal subjects.

CARR. I'm sorry there are not more of them.

STEELE (*going toward the door*). I hope you'll remember what I said about Crispus Attucks. He's very dangerous.

(CALDWELL, *a man in his forties, enters in time to hear* STEELE *mention* ATTUCKS' *name.*)

CARR. I'll remember it, sir. Can you get out all right?

STEELE (*as he goes out*). Yes, you needn't come down.

(CARR *holds the door open until* STEELE *is down the stairs.*)

CALDWELL (*anxiously, as* CARR *closes the door*). What did he say?

CARR. He said Mr. Attucks is a fugitive slave and has been for years.

CALDWELL. We know that.

CARR. I didn't.

CALDWELL. Did he say anything else?

CARR. That his former master is offering ten pounds for his capture and return.

CALDWELL. So it's gone as far as that, has it?

CARR. And the British will be looking for him today.

CALDWELL. In that case, Attucks must be warned. (*He starts toward the door but stops reconsidering.*) No, that won't be necessary. He'll be watchful, and he isn't afraid.

CARR. You consider him a bold man, do you?

CALDWELL. Yes, absolutely fearless.

CARR. And you and Mr. Gray and Mr. Maverick think a great deal of him.

CALDWELL. As all men think of brave leaders in their cause.

CARR (*sitting above the table*). I wish that you four were as diligent in the cause of the mother country.

CALDWELL. Are you diligent in her cause, Mr. Carr?

CARR. I believe in her cause.

CALDWELL. To be taxed by the British without being represented in the Parliament, to be overrun by foreign soldiers —do such things as these justify your calling the British cause the right one?

CARR (*going to the window*). A mother is always wiser than her children.

CALDWELL. A true mother is always kind to her children.

CARR (*looking out of the window*). Here comes Crispus Attucks now.

CALDWELL (*going to the window and looking out*). How can you say that a man who carries himself as he does, who is intelligent, brave, and born to leadership, is allied with the wrong cause?

CARR. All men who are allied with any cause think their cause is the right one, Mr. Caldwell.

CALDWELL. You are inclined to be just, Mr. Carr. I hope some day your eyes will be opened.

CARR. It will take something more than words to destroy my loyalty to the British Crown. (*He goes to the door and opens it, and* CRISPUS ATTUCKS *enters. He is a dignified black man in his late forties, dressed in the same style as the others. His appearance is that of a thinker and leader.*)

ATTUCKS. Good evening, gentlemen.

CARR. Good evening, Mr. Attucks.

CALDWELL. You walked through the streets undisturbed, I hope.

ATTUCKS. Yes. The soldiers are boisterous, but I passed along as peacefully as usual.

CALDWELL. Have you heard the latest news?

ATTUCKS. So far as I know the news is the same as it was yesterday except that the situation is nearer the boiling point.

CALDWELL. I mean the news that concerns you personally.

CARR (*who has sat at the desk*). Mr. Attucks, do you know that you are being hunted as a fugitive slave, and that there is a reward on your head?

ATTUCKS (*smiling for the first time*). That does not surprise me, Mr. Carr. All I can say is that I will never be taken back to slavery. But I don't consider my former owner as an opponent worthy of a second thought. My chief enemies are King George and the British soldiers.

CALDWELL. But you must be careful not to be captured. We need you.

ATTUCKS. I will be careful in order to be free to attack the British soldiers in our streets.

CALDWELL (*surprised*). You mean to attack them?

ATTUCKS. Yes, even if I must attack them alone.

CALDWELL. You will not have to attack them alone.

ATTUCKS. Then you are with me?

CALDWELL. Yes.

CARR (*rising*). Mr. Attucks.

ATTUCKS. Yes, Mr. Carr.

CARR. You know I am a loyal subject of the British Crown, don't you?

ATTUCKS. I had thought so.

CARR. Then, as such, you cannot expect me to be sympathetic with your attitude towards my sovereign.

ATTUCKS. Mr. Carr, I expect nothing from anyone except those who hate oppression. If you do not love liberty enough to consider yourself a free citizen of these colonies, I expect no more from you than I do from a soldier of your king.

CARR. It is not as an enemy I speak to you. Actually, I admire everything about you—everything except your rebellious spirit. But I must ask you not to come to these rooms above the shop again.

ATTUCKS (*quietly*). My coming here in the future may not be necessary. I hope to take some action this evening that will keep the British soldiers from marching over citizens in the Boston streets.

CALDWELL (*addressing* CARR). Mr. Carr, if Mr. Attucks is refused admittance here I will not come again and neither will any of our friends.

CARR. I'm sorry, but I've been far too lenient with all of you. I must make some show of loyalty if I am to keep my shop open.

ATTUCKS. Is it loyalty that drives you to that decision or is it fear of your friends?

CARR. Loyalty, Mr. Attucks. I fear no one.

ATTUCKS. Not even the king of Britain?

CARR. I have no cause to fear the king of Britain.

ATTUCKS. Someday it may be proved to you that you have allied yourself with the wrong side—the most brutal and unjust side.

CARR. I think the Crown is neither brutal nor unjust.

ATTUCKS. If you saw those British soldiers shoot down unarmed citizens instead of merely insulting them, I suppose you would still cast your lot with the more powerful and think they were just and kind.

CARR. I do not approve of bloodshed.

ATTUCKS. None of us approves of bloodshed, but all of us may see it before many days.

CARR. I hope not. I earnestly hope not.

ATTUCKS. And if blood is spilled, whose blood do you think it will be?

CALDWELL. Who has the arms?

ATTUCKS. Surely you do not think it will be the blood of the soldiers when the citizens, your neighbors, are unarmed.

CARR (*looking out of the window*). If the citizens would retire to their homes—

ATTUCKS. Be driven from their own streets by soldiers from thousands of miles away?

CARR (*going to the door*). I must go down. Soldiers are coming into the shop. (*He goes out.*)

ATTUCKS (*indicating Carr*). He's a good man. He should be on the side of the colonists. (*To* CALDWELL.) Our friends are a little late, aren't they?

CALDWELL (*going to the window and looking out*). Yes, but they'll be here.

ATTUCKS. Something must be done and done soon.

CALDWELL. Yes, this situation can't go on much longer. (*Interested in something outside.*) Look, Mr. Attucks. (ATTUCKS *goes nearer the window.*)

CALDWELL (*pointing*). Do you see that officer coming this way?

ATTUCKS. Yes.

CALDWELL. Do you know him?

ATTUCKS. No. Who is he?

CALDWELL. Major Evering. They say he's one of the cruelest officers in the British army.

ATTUCKS. He seems to be coming here.

CALDWELL. You don't think he saw you come in, do you?

ATTUCKS. I'm not sure.

CALDWELL. He's coming in. Wait a minute, I'll find out. (*He opens the door and listens, then goes outside, but returns quickly.*)

CALDWELL (*excitedly*). He's coming up the stairs! You must hide!

ATTUCKS. Why?

CALDWELL. He may be looking for you! Are you armed?

ATTUCKS. No.

CALDWELL. Then you must hide! We can't have you taken! We need you too much! This way! (*He pushes* ATTUCKS *towards the wardrobe and opens the door.* ATTUCKS *goes in reluctantly.*) Do this much for our cause.

(CALDWELL *closes the door and goes back to the left of the window. There is a loud knock on the door.*)

CALDWELL (*moving to the left of the table*). Come in!

(MAJOR EVERING *enters. He is a handsome man about forty-five, dressed in the red coat and other regalia of the British officer.*)

MAJOR EVERING (*with an air of superiority*). I am Major Evering of His Majesty's forces. What is your name?

CALDWELL. My name is Caldwell.

MAJOR EVERING. John Caldwell, I suppose.

CALDWELL. No, Emanuel Caldwell.

MAJOR EVERING (*standing at the right of the table and taking off his gloves*). A loyal subject of King George III?

CALDWELL. A loyal citizen of these colonies, Sir.

MAJOR EVERING (*bitterly*). By that you mean a potential rebel!

CALDWELL. I mean I am a colonist.

MAJOR EVERING. A rebel whose name is Emanuel Caldwell.

CALDWELL. Yes, if you must have it that way.

MAJOR EVERING. You could have told me your full name in the beginning. Why didn't you?

CALDWELL. I didn't think it necessary.

MAJOR EVERING. By the same course of reasoning you think it unnecessary to be loyal to your king?

CALDWELL (*angered by the officer's manner*). I will not answer that question.

MAJOR EVERING (*whose manner becomes more and more overbearing*). Then answer this one: Do you know a man—a black man—named Crispus Attucks?

CALDWELL. Yes, I know of him.

MAJOR EVERING. I saw him enter the tobacco shop a while ago, but did not see him come out. Is he here?

CALDWELL. No.

MAJOR EVERING. I suppose you know he is a fugitive slave with a reward on his head.

CALDWELL. I had heard that.

MAJOR EVERING. So you have no knowledge of his whereabouts?

CALDWELL. I have not.

MAJOR EVERING. I believe you are lying!

CALDWELL (*fully angered*). You may believe what you wish!

MAJOR EVERING. Your tongue is becoming sharp! I wish your sword were as sharp!

CALDWELL. I do not carry a sword and would not except in time of war!

MAJOR EVERING (*moving closer to* CALDWELL). And in time of war you would not carry a sword—you would carry a gun!

CALDWELL. Which I hope would be aimed at you!

MAJOR EVERING. Dirty rebel! (*He strikes* CALDWELL *across the face with his gloves*). That should soften your tongue! (*As* CALDWELL *starts for him,* MAJOR EVERING *steps back and draws his sword.*) Come another step and I'll run you through! I should run you through anyway! I should make you get down on your knees and take back every word you've said! Down on your knees, you rebel dog. Down! (CALDWELL *refuses to kneel.*) I'll order you once more, and if you refuse to kneel I'll cut you down! (ATTUCKS *comes from the wardrobe with the gun aimed from his hip at* MAJOR EVERING.)

ATTUCKS (*in a firm voice*). Stand where you are and lower your sword!

MAJOR EVERING (*staring in surprise*). What!

ATTUCKS. Put down your sword!

MAJOR EVERING (*without lowering the point of his sword*). By God! By what right do you—

ATTUCKS (*threateningly*). Lower your sword, Major Evering!

MAJOR EVERING. I refuse! Who are you to demand that I lower my sword?

ATTUCKS. I am Crispus Attucks! Surrender your sword to Mr. Caldwell!

MAJOR EVERING (*lowering his sword*). You cannot take me prisoner! I am an officer of King George!

ATTUCKS (*grimly*). I am a desperate black man, Major Evering! I neither expect nor give quarter! I may not be able to imprison you, but I will kill you if you do not give up your sword! Surrender your sword to Mr. Caldwell, at once!

(*Seeing determination in* ATTUCK'S *eyes*, MAJOR EVERING *reverses his sword and gives it to* CALDWELL, *who puts it on the table.*)

ATTUCKS (*to* CALDWELL). Now, get some towels from that wardrobe.

MAJOR EVERING. What do you mean to do?

ATTUCKS. I mean to bind and gag you and hide you away for a while.

MAJOR EVERING. You can't do that! They'll hang you! (CALDWELL, *who has gone into the wardrobe, comes out with some towels.*)

ATTUCKS (*to* CALDWELL). I want you to tie his hands behind him. (*To* MAJOR EVERING.) Put your hands behind you!

MAJOR EVERING (*putting his hands behind him*). I'll see that this will be the last rebel act you commit!

ATTUCKS. I have other plans more important than this.

MAJOR EVERING. Your other plans will never be carried out after this is made known!

ATTUCKS. This will not be found out until my other plans are completed.

(CALDWELL *has tied the major's hands and is still standing behind him.*)

ATTUCKS. Now gag him.

MAJOR EVERING (*almost exploding*). This is an outrage!

ATTUCKS. So you inferred before, Major Evering; open your mouth!

MAJOR EVERING. I will not!

ATTUCKS. Move from behind him, Mr. Caldwell! (*As* CALDWELL *moves aside,* ATTUCKS *moves forward so that the muzzle of the gun touches* MAJOR EVERING'S *chest.*)

ATTUCKS. Now open your mouth! (MAJOR EVERING *opens his mouth.*) Gag him. (CALDWELL *puts the towel in* EVERING'S *mouth and knots it at the back of his head.*) Cover his ears. (CALDWELL *puts a towel over his head and knots it under his chin so that his ears are covered.*) Now put him into the wardrobe and tie his feet together. (CALDWELL *pushes* EVERING *into the wardrobe and ties his feet together.* ATTUCKS *leans the gun in the corner, then takes* MAJOR EVERING'S *sword from the table and puts it into the wardrobe.*) The storm has just begun.

CALDWELL. The storm?

ATTUCKS. Yes. What I have planned will strike Boston and the whole army like a storm; and besides, a man about to die never fears to use any means to gain his end.

CALDWELL. Why do you say "about to die"?

ATTUCKS. I mean that I will die before I go back to slavery.

CALDWELL. I can never blame you for that.

ATTUCKS. And I mean I will die to prove to the British that there is fighting spirit among the colonists. I plan to face the soldiers in the street today even if I have to face them alone!

CALDWELL. You will not have to face them alone!

ATTUCKS (*listening*). Someone is coming up the stairs!

(*He takes the gun from the corner and stands ready as* CALDWELL *opens the door.* GRAY *and* MAVERICK, *the two they have been expecting, enter. They are men between forty and fifty years of age.*)

GRAY. Good evening, gentlemen. (*He notices the gun in* AT-TUCK'*s hands*). Why the warlike appearance?

ATTUCKS (*putting the gun in the corner*). They tell me I am being hunted.

MAVERICK. Why hunted, Mr. Attucks?

ATTUCKS. Hunted at a fugitive slave.

GRAY. Absurd!

CALDWELL. Absurd, but true.

ATTUCKS. Yes, the soldiers are already hunting me. They may be here in force within an hour, but by that time I hope our plan will be carried through.

GRAY. What plan?

ATTUCKS. Before we go into that I think it is only fair to tell you that we have a British officer bound and gagged in that wardrobe. (*He points to the wardrobe.*)

MAVERICK. You're joking.

CALDWELL (*going to the wardrobe and holding up the sword*). The British sword, gentlemen! (*Not wholly convinced,* GRAY *and* MAVERICK *go to the wardrobe and look in.*)

GRAY (*astonished*). How did you do it?

ATTUCKS. He came here hunting me and was about to attack Mr. Caldwell with his sword, so we were forced to take him prisoner.

MAVERICK. And what do you intend doing with him now that he's your prisoner?

ATTUCKS. We'll keep him here until we come to some understanding with the army.

GRAY. But we can't come to any understanding with them. They won't listen to us.

ATTUCKS. We'll make them listen.

MAVERICK. How can we make them listen?

ATTUCKS. We'll confront them in the street, and if they refuse to listen we'll attack them.

GRAY *and* MAVERICK (*together*). Attack them!

ATTUCKS. If reasoning fails, then the only way to get rid of these soldiers is to attack them.

GRAY. Doesn't that mean a great risk?

ATTUCKS. I am here to risk my life.

MAVERICK (*doubtfully*). Blood will surely be spilt, Mr. Attucks.

ATTUCKS. Then let it be my blood! Do you realize that these soldiers attack men, insult women, and trample upon little children in the streets?

GRAY. That may be true, but—

ATTUCKS. Do you realize that they came from three thousand miles across the sea to force us to pay taxes when we have no voice in saying how much we shall pay or when we shall pay it?

CALDWELL. We realize all that, but we must reason before acting too hastily.

ATTUCKS. Of course. I have been a chattel slave, and I appreciate freedom more than you do.

MAVERICK. Not more than we do.

ATTUCKS. At any rate, I will give my life for freedom. Will you?

MAVERICK. That depends.

CALDWELL (*to* ATTUCKS). I will go wherever you go and do whatever you do for freedom.

ATTUCKS. Well said, Mr. Caldwell. I will lead. Will all of you follow me?

CALDWELL. I will.

ATTUCKS. Are we two to go alone?

GRAY. No, I will go.

MAVERICK. And I.

ATTUCKS. Then we will go together with our minds set on one thing. Are you ready, gentlemen?

THE OTHERS. Yes. (*As they start to the door,* CARR *enters excitedly.*)

CARR. They have destroyed my goods! They have looted my store!

CALDWELL. Who has?

CARR. The British soldiers!

ATTUCKS. In spite of your being friendly to them? In spite of your being friendly to the Crown?

CARR. Yes, in spite of everything they have ruined me!

ATTUCKS. And you still don't consider them unfair and brutal?

CARR (*speaking grimly*). I may have to take back some of the things I've said, Mr. Attucks.

CALDWELL. This kind of thing will drive all the colonists together in the end.

GRAY (*putting his hand on* CARR's *shoulder*). I'm sorry, Mr. Carr.

CARR (*looking about*). Didn't Major Evering come up here?

CALDWELL. Yes.

CARR. Where is he? I didn't see him go out.

ATTUCKS. Mr. Carr, Major Evering is bound and gagged in your wardrobe.

CARR (*astonished*). Bound and gagged! (*He rushes to the wardrobe*).

ATTUCKS. We were forced to imprison him.

CARR. But—but—look what a position that leaves me in!

CALDWELL. He is bound and gagged and his ears are covered so that he can't hear anything.

CARR. I can't allow this in my place!

ATTUCKS (*firmly*). You must allow it! We must have your word of honor that you will not free him for an hour!

CARR. And if I refuse to give my word—

ATTUCKS. Then we shall be forced to bind and gag you and imprison you with him.

GRAY (*diplomatically*). If you are wise, Mr. Carr, you will forget about all this for now. In about an hour, you can come back up here and act surprised and horrified to find Major Evering imprisoned in your wardrobe.

CALDWELL. Evering will be none the wiser. He can't hear what we are saying because his ears are covered.

MAVERICK. And besides, you owe him nothing. Compare what the British have done for you to what they have done against you.

CARR (*looking uncertainly from one to the other*). I suppose there is nothing else for me to do.

ATTUCKS. And do we have your word of honor that you will leave him there for an hour?

CARR (*reluctantly*). Yes.

MAVERICK. Think of the wrong they have done you and you will feel more contented to do something for the cause of freedom.

ATTUCKS (*extending his hand, which* CARR *takes*). Good luck, Mr. Carr. I hope before many days your opinion of our enemies will be the same as ours.

CARR (*with uncertainty*). I don't know, Mr. Attucks. I find it hard to determine anything at the moment.

ATTUCKS (*to the others*). Gentlemen, let us go.

(*He goes out, followed by* GRAY, CALDWELL, *and* MAV-
ERICK. *When they have gone,* CARR *stands looking at the
wardrobe with indecision; then as if fully decided on his
course of action he goes to the window and is looking down
into the street when* STEELE *enters hurriedly.*)

STEELE. Mr. Carr, those men—the ones who just left here—
where are they going?

CARR. They said they were going out to confront the soldiers
in the street and lead an attack against them if necessary.

STEELE. What! Attack the soldiers?

CARR. That seems to be their plan.

STEELE. What can those four do against a company of trained
soldiers?

CARR (*pointing through the window*). But look out there.
There are hundreds of people.

STEELE. Hundreds—but unarmed. They will be like children
confronting armed soldiers.

CARR (*whose tone and manner have changed from what they
were at the beginning of the play*). They can at least make
the soldiers know what they want.

STEELE. What do they want? (*Then he looks at* CARR *closely.*)
Mr. Carr, your tone seems to be somewhat different from
what it was when I was here earlier.

CARR (*turning to him*). Did you see how my store was
wrecked, Mr. Steele?

STEELE. Yes, how did that happen?

CARR. The soldiers looted it.

STEELE. That's very unfortunate, Mr. Carr, very unfortunate.

CARR (*with a hint of sarcasm in his voice*). And in spite of
that I am expected to be loyal to the king and the king's
men.

STEELE. Loyalty is not a matter of pounds and shillings, Mr.
Carr.

CARR. No, but a livelihood is, and without a livelihood there can hardly be much loyalty.

STEELE. Your talk is rebellious, sir!

(*As* CARR *is about to reply, there is a great noise in the street. Both men go to the window.*)

CARR (*excitedly*). Look! Attucks is leading the citizens against the soldiers!

STEELE. And the soldiers are about to shoot them down! (*There is a loud report outside.*)   .

CARR. God! Attucks is down! Caldwell, Gray, and Maverick are down! It's a massacre!

STEELE (*angrily*). They brought is upon themselves! What did you expect?

CARR (*moving from the window in a state of mental agony*). I never expected to live to see this!

STEELE. They deserved it!

CARR. A citizen never deserves death for asserting his rights!

STEELE. Are you mad, Mr. Carr?

CARR (*enraged*). Yes, I am mad! I have been a loyal subject of the king, but no more! His soldiers have wronged me! Wronged all of us!

STEELE. What are you saying?

CARR (*taking the gun from the corner*). I'm saying that those citizens who have been killed must be avenged! (*He fires at the wardrobe.*)

STEELE. What did that mean?

CARR. Major Evering was bound and gagged in that wardrobe!

STEELE (*staggered*). My God! (*As he starts towards the wardrobe, the curtain falls.*)

TALKING ABOUT THE PLAY

1. Mr. Carr is an important character in this play because it is his personality and way of thinking that changes at the end. What kind of person is he at the beginning of the play? Pick out some lines which clearly exhibit his feeling and loyalties. What evidence is there in the beginning of the play that Carr will change in personality and loyalty?

2. Because of what others say about him, we learn a great deal about Crispus Attucks even before he comes on the stage. What impressions do you get about him? Are all of your impressions favorable? Are any negative? What specific things do the men say which tell you a great deal about Attucks' character?

3. In speaking about Attucks, Carr says, "All men who are allied with any cause think their cause is the right one." What does he mean by that statement? What insight does this statement give us about Carr and Attucks?

4. What additional impressions does Attucks give you about himself when he appears on stage? In what way is the opinion the men had about him earlier justified by Attucks himself?

5. What do you think of Attucks' plan to lead the colonists against the British soldiers? Is he being foolhardy, or is there another motive behind his plans? Explain.

6. What kind of man is Major Evering? What function does he have in the play? In what way would the play suffer if Evering were omitted completely?

7. At one point, Attucks says, "A man about to die never fears to use any means to gain his end." What does he mean by this? What is Attucks' "end"? Is this really the best solution Attucks could work out for the situation?

8. What incident helps Carr to change his viewpoint? Do you think the change is convincing? Why or why not? Do you feel Carr's change is permanent?
9. Compare the reactions of Steele and Carr as they watch what happens when Attucks and his friends face the British soldiers in the street. What is the striking difference in their reactions?
10. What do you think of Carr's act of vengeance at the end of the play? Was he justified in what he did? Explain.
11. Does the title of this play in any way indicate what the climax and end might be? Explain.

FOR YOUR OWN WRITING

1. Can you think of any modern-day hero who performed an act similar to Attucks'? Describe this act and state what qualities this person had which enabled him to act heroically.
2. When speaking to Caldwell, Maverick, and Gray, Attucks says, "I have been a chattel slave, and I appreciate freedom more than you do." Write a paragraph in which you discuss how the reason behind this statement might have helped Attucks decide to fight for freedom.
3. Allegiance to one's country and standing up for what one believes are very important matters to young people today. What are some of the reasons why someone might have a strong allegiance to a country or a cause? What traits must be evident in someone to feel this way?

I REMEMBER MAMA

JOHN VAN DRUTEN

I REMEMBER MAMA

What attitudes create a happy family life? What kind of family would you most like to grow up in?

I Remember Mama shows the Hansen family. They don't have fame or wealth, but they do have love and happiness. The members of the family are very different people, with different personalities; and yet they live together, help and support one another, and talk to each other about important things. As you read this play, watch for the individual family members—how they are alike, and how they are different. But look, too, at the family as a whole—how they get along, how they act and feel toward each other.

This short play is an *excerpt*, or selected part, of a three-act stage play by the same title. Look at the scene description on page 96. Try to visualize the arrangement of the two small revolving stages in front of the main stage. These small stages, holding very simplified scenery, permit actors to move easily and quickly from one setting to another (as from the drug-store counter to the kitchen) without requiring long waits or hurried moving of scenery. In the full-length version of the play, the small stages are used even more often, to represent different places and to permit rapid changes of scene.

Notice, too, later in the excerpt, how the passing of time is indicated by the blackout and the curtain.

CHARACTERS

MAMA

KATRIN

A SODA CLERK

DAGMAR

PAPA

NELS

MR. HYDE

CHRISTINE

AUNT JENNY

SCENE. *On either side of the stage, down front, are two small revolving stages, left and right, on which some of the scenes are played against very simplified backgrounds. As each scene finishes, the lights dim and the scene revolves out, leaving a clear view of the main stage. The main stage is raised by two steps, above which curtains open and close.*

MAMA *and* KATRIN *have just come from the hospital where they have visited the youngest daughter,* DAGMAR, *about to come home after a month's illness.* DAGMAR *has been looking forward to seeing her pet cat, which she calls Uncle Elizabeth.*

MAMA. Katrin, you like we go next door, and I treat you to an ice-cream soda?

KATRIN (*overcome*). Mama—do you mean it?

MAMA. Sure. We celebrate. We celebrate that Dagmar is well, and coming home again. (*They cross to the left, where the revolving stage represents a drugstore, with a table and two chairs, at which they seat themselves.*) What you like to have, Katrin?

KATRIN. I think a chocolate . . . no, a strawberry . . . no, a chocolate soda.

MAMA (*smiling*). You are sure?

KATRIN (*gravely*). I think so. But, Mama, can we afford it?

MAMA. I think this once we can afford it. (*The* SODA CLERK *appears from left.*)

SODA CLERK. What's it going to be ladies?

MAMA. A chocolate ice-cream soda, please—and a cup of coffee. (*The* SODA CLERK *goes.*)

KATRIN. Mama, he called us "ladies"! (MAMA *smiles.*) Why aren't you having a soda, too?

MAMA. Better I like coffee.

KATRIN. When can I drink coffee?

MAMA. When you are grown up.

KATRIN. When I am eighteen?

MAMA. Maybe before that.

KATRIN. When I graduate?

MAMA. Maybe. I don't know. Comes the day you are grown up, Papa and I will know.

KATRIN. Is coffee really nicer than soda?

MAMA. When you are grown up it is.

KATRIN. Did you used to like sodas better . . . before you were grown up?

MAMA. We didn't have sodas before I was grown up. It was in the old country.

KATRIN (*astonished*). You mean they don't have sodas in Norway?

MAMA. Now, maybe. Now I think they have many things from America. But not when I was a little girl. (*The* SODA CLERK *brings the soda and the coffee.*)

SODA CLERK. There you are, folks. (*He sets them on the table and departs.*)

KATRIN (*after a good pull on the soda*). Mama, do you ever want to go back to the old country?

MAMA. I like to go back once to look, maybe. To see the mountains and the fjords. I like to show them once to you all. When Dagmar is big, maybe we all go back home once . . . one summer . . . like tourists. But that is how it would be. I would be tourist there now. There is no one I would know any more. And maybe we see the little house where Papa and I live when we first marry. And . . . (*Her eyes grow misty and thoughtful.*) something else I would look at.

KATRIN. What is that? (MAMA *does not answer.*) What would you look at, Mama?

MAMA. Katrin, you do not know you have brother? Besides Nels?

KATRIN. No! A brother? In Norway? Mama . . .

MAMA. He is my first baby.

KATRIN. Is he there now?

MAMA (*simply*). He is dead.

KATRIN (*disappointed*). Oh, I thought you meant . . . I thought you meant a real brother. A long-lost one, like in stories. When did he die?

MAMA. When he is two year old. It is his grave I would like to see again. (*She is suddenly near tears, biting her lip and stirring her coffee violently, spilling a few drops on her suit. She gets her handkerchief from her pocketbook, dabs at her skirt, then briefly at her nose; then she returns the handkerchief and turns to* KATRIN *again.*)

MAMA (*matter-of-factly*). Is good, your ice-cream soda?

KATRIN (*more interested now in* MAMA *than in it*). Yes. Mama . . . have you had a very hard life?

MAMA (*surprised*). Hard? No. No life is easy all the time. It is not meant to be.

KATRIN. But . . . rich people . . . aren't their lives easy?

MAMA. I don't know Katrin. I have never known rich people. But I see them sometimes in stores and in the streets, and they do not look as if they were easy.

KATRIN. Wouldn't you like to be rich?

MAMA. I would like to be rich the way I would like to be ten feet high. Would be good for some things—bad for others.

KATRIN. But didn't you come to America to get rich?

MAMA (*shocked*). No. We come to America because they are all here—all the others. Is good for families to be together.

KATRIN. And did you like it right away?

MAMA. Right away. When we get off the ferry boat and I see San Francisco and all the family, I say: "Is like Norway," only it is better than Norway. And then you are all born here, and I become American citizen. But not to get rich.

KATRIN. I want to be rich. Rich and famous. I'd buy you your warm coat. When are you going to get that coat, Mama?

MAMA. Soon now, maybe—when we pay doctor, and Mr. Hyde pay his rent. I think now I *must* ask him. I ask him tomorrow, after Dagmar comes home.

KATRIN. When I'm rich and famous, I'll buy you lovely clothes. White satin gowns with long trains to them. And jewelry. I'll buy you a pearl necklace.

MAMA. We talk too much! (*She signs to the* SODA CLERK.) Come, finish your soda. We must go home. (*The* SODA CLERK *comes.*) How much it is, please?

SODA CLERK. Fifteen cents.

MAMA. Here are two dimes. You keep the nickel. And thank you. Was good coffee. (*They start out and up the steps towards the curtains.*) Tomorrow Dagmar will be home again. And, Katrin, you see Uncle Elizabeth is there. This afternoon again she was asking for him. You keep Uncle

Elizabeth in the house all day until she comes home.

(*They disappear behind the curtains. After a second, the howls of a cat in pain are heard from behind the curtains— low at first, then rising to a heart-rending volume, and then diminishing again as the curtains part on the kitchen.* MAMA, PAPA, *and* DAGMAR *are entering the house.*)

DAGMAR (*standing on threshold, listening joyfully*). It's Uncle Elizabeth, welcoming me home! That's his song of welcome. Where is he, Mama? (*She looks around for the source of the howls.*)

MAMA. He is in the pantry. . . . (*As* DAGMAR *starts to rush to the pantry door*) But wait . . . wait a minute, Dagmar. I must tell you. Uncle Elizabeth is . . . sick.

DAGMAR. Sick? What's the matter with him?

PAPA. He has been in a fight. Last night. He come home this morning very sick indeed.

(DAGMAR *starts for the pantry door, back right, as* NELS *comes out.*)

MAMA. Nels, how is Uncle Elizabeth? Nels has been doctoring him.

NELS. He's pretty bad, Mama. I've dressed all his wounds again with boric acid, but . . . (*As* DAGMAR *tries to get past him*) I wouldn't go and see him now, baby.

DAGMAR. I've got to. He's my cat. I haven't seen him in a whole month. Move. (*She runs into the pantry and disappears.*)

MAMA. Nels, what you think?

NELS. I think we ought to have had him put away before she came home.

MAMA. But she would have been so unhappy if he was not here at all.

NELS. She'll be unhappier still if he dies.

(*Another howl is heard from the pantry, and then* DAGMAR *comes rushing back.*)

DAGMAR. Mama, what happened to him? What happened to him? Oh, Mama . . . when I tried to pick him up, his bandage slipped over his eye. It was bleeding. Oh, Mama, it looked awful. Oh . . . (*She starts to cry.*)

MAMA (*fondling her*). He look like that all over. Nels, you go see to his eye again.

(*Wearily,* NELS *returns to the pantry.*)

MAMA. Listen, Dagmar, would it not be better for the poor thing to go quietly to sleep?

DAGMAR. You mean—go to sleep and never wake up again? (MAMA *nods gently.*) No.

PAPA. I think he die, anyway. Nels try to make him well. But I do not think he can.

DAGMAR. Mama can. Mama can do everything. (*Another howl from offstage. She clutches* MAMA *agonizedly.*) Make him live, Mama. Make him well again. *Please!*

MAMA. We see. Let us see how he gets through the night. And now, Dagmar, you must go to bed. I bring you your supper.

DAGMAR. But you will fix Uncle Elizabeth? You promise, Mama?

MAMA. I promise I try. Go now. (DAGMAR *goes out, back left.*) I must fix her supper. (*She starts for the pantry. Howls again. She and* PAPA *stand and look at each other.* NELS *comes out.*)

NELS. Mama, it's just cruelty, keeping that cat alive.

MAMA. I know.

PAPA (*as another howl the loudest yet emerges*). You say we see how the cat get through the night. I ask you how do *we* get through the night? Is no use, Marta. We must put the cat to sleep. Nels, you go to the drugstore, and get something. Some chloroform, maybe. (*He gives him a coin.*)

NELS. How much shall I get?

PAPA. You ask the man. You tell him it is for a cat. He knows. (NELS *goes out left.* PAPA *looks at* MAMA's *face.*) Is best. Is the only thing.

MAMA. I know. But poor Dagmar. It is a sad homecoming for her. And she has been so good in hospital. Never once she cry. (*She pulls herself together.*) I get her supper. (*Another howl from off stage*) And I take the cat outside. Right outside, where we . . . where Dagmar cannot hear him.

(*She goes into the pantry.* PAPA *takes a folded newspaper from his pocket, puts on his glasses and starts to read. The door, back left, opens gently and* MR. HYDE *peeps out. He wears his hat and coat and carries his suitcase and a letter.* PAPA *has his back to him.* MR. HYDE *lays the letter on the dresser and then starts to tiptoe across to the door. Then* PAPA *sees him.*)

PAPA. You go out, Mr. Hyde?

MR. HYDE (*pretending surprise*). Oh . . . oh, I did not see you, Mr. Hansen. (*He puts down the suitcase.*) I did not know you were back. As a matter of fact, I . . . I was about to leave this letter for you. (*He fetches it.*) The fact is . . . I . . . I have been called away.

PAPA. So?

MR. HYDE. A letter I received this morning necessitates my departure. My immediate departure.

PAPA. *I am sorry.* (MAMA *returns with a tray, on which are milk, bread, butter, and jelly.*)

PAPA. Mama, Mr. Hyde says he goes away.

MAMA (*coming to the table with the tray*). Is true?

MR. HYDE. Alas, dear Madam, yes. 'Tis true, 'tis pity. And pity 'tis, 'tis true. You will find here . . . (*He presents the letter.*) my check for all I owe you, and a note expressing my profoundest thanks for all your kind hospitality. You will say goodnight to the children for me? (*He bows as* MAMA *takes the letter.*)

MAMA (*distressed*). Sure. Sure.

MR. HYDE (*bowing again*). Madam, my deepest gratitude. (*He kisses her hand.* MAMA *looks astonished. He bows to* PAPA.) Sir—my sincerest admiration! (*He opens the street door.*) It has been a privilege. *Ave atque vale!* Hail and farewell! (*He makes a gesture and goes.*)

MAMA. Was wonderful man! Is too bad. (*She opens the letter, takes out the check.*)

PAPA. How much is check for?

MAMA. Hundred ten dollar! Is four months.

PAPA. Good. Good.

MAMA. Is wonderful. Now we pay doctor everything.

PAPA. And you buy your warm coat. With fur now, maybe.

MAMA (*sadly*). But there will be no more reading. You take the check, Lars. You get the money?

PAPA (*taking it*). Sure, I get it. What does he say in his letter?

MAMA. You read it while I fix supper for Dagmar. (*She starts to butter the bread and spread jelly, while* PAPA *reads.*)

PAPA (*reading*). "Dear friends, I find myself compelled to take a somewhat hasty departure from this house of happiness . . ."

MAMA. Is beautiful letter.

PAPA (*continuing*). "I am leaving you my library for the children . . ."

MAMA. He leaves his books?

PAPA. He says so.

MAMA. But is wonderful. Go see, Lars. See if they are in his room. (PAPA *lays down the letter and goes out back left.* NELS *and* CHRISTINE *appear down left, coming up to the house.* CHRISTINE *carries schoolbooks.*)

CHRISTINE. I'm sure it was him, Nels. Carrying his suitcase, and getting on the cable car. I'm sure he's going away.

NELS. Well, I hope he's paid Mama. (*They open the street door.*)

CHRISTINE (*bursting in*). Mama, I saw Mr. Hyde getting on the cable car.

MAMA. I know. He leave.

CHRISTINE. Did he pay you?

MAMA. Sure, he pay me. Hundred ten dollar . . .

NELS. Gee. . . .

MAMA (*smiling*). Is good.

CHRISTINE. Are you going to put it in the bank?

MAMA. We need it right away. (PAPA *returns, staggering under an armload of books.*) Mr. Hyde leaves his books, too. (PAPA *stacks them on the table.* NELS *and* CHRISTINE *rush to them, reading titles.*)

NELS. Say! *The Pickwick Papers, The Complete Shakespeare* . . .

CHRISTINE. *Alice in Wonderland, The Oxford Book of Verse* . . .

NELS. *The Last of the Mohicans, Ivanhoe* . . .

CHRISTINE. We were right in the middle of that.

MAMA. Nels can finish that. He can read to us now in the evenings. He has fine voice, too, like Mr. Hyde. (NELS *flushes with pleasure.*) Is wonderful. So much we can learn. (*She finishes making supper.*) Christine, you take the butter back to the cooler for me, and the yelly, too. (CHRISTINE *does*.) I go up to Dagmar now. (*She lifts the tray, then pauses*.) You get it, Nels?

NELS. What? . . . Oh . . . (*Taking a druggist's small bottle from his pocket*.) Here.

MAMA. You put it down. After I come back, we do it. You know how?

NELS. Why, no, Mama, I . . .

MAMA. You do not ask?

NELS. No, I . . . I thought Papa . . .

MAMA. You know, Lars?

PAPA. No, I don't *know* . . . but it cannot be difficult. If you *hold* the cat . . .

MAMA. And watch him die? No! I think you better get rags . . . and a big sponge, to soak up the chloroform. You put it in the box with him, and cover him up. You get them ready out there.

NELS. Sure, Mama.

MAMA. I bring some blankets.

(NELS *goes off to the pantry, as* CHRISTINE *comes back. Again* MAMA *lifts the tray and starts for the door back left. But there is a knock on the street door from* AUNT JENNY, *who has come to the house from down left in a state of excitement*.)

MAMA (*agitated*). So much goes on! See who it is Christine.

CHRISTINE (*peeping*). It's Aunt Jenny. (*She opens the door*.)

MAMA. Jenny. . . .

JENNY (*breathless*). Marta . . . has he gone?

MAMA. Who?

JENNY. Your boarder . . . Mr. Hyde . . .

MAMA. Yes, he has gone. Why?

JENNY. Did he pay you?

MAMA. Sure he pay me.

JENNY. How?

MAMA. He give me check. Lars has it right there.

JENNY (*with meaning*). A check!

MAMA. Jenny, what is it? Christine, you give Dagmar her supper. (CHRISTINE *takes the tray from her and goes out back left.*) What is it, Jenny? How do you know that Mr. Hyde is gone?

JENNY. I was at Mr. Kruper's down the street . . . you know the restaurant and bakery . . . and he told me Mr. Hyde was there today having his lunch, and when he left he asked if he would cash a check for him. For fifty dollars. (*She pauses.*)

PAPA. Well, go on.

JENNY. Your fine Mr. Hyde didn't expect Mr. Kruper to take it to bank until tomorrow, but he did. And what do you think? Mr. Hyde hasn't even an *account* at that bank! (NELS *returns and stands in the pantry doorway.*)

MAMA. I don't understand.

PAPA (*taking the check from his pocket*). You mean the check is no good?

JENNY. No good at all. (*Triumphantly*) Your Mr. Hyde was a crook, just as I always thought he was, for all his reading and fine ways. Mr. Kruper said he'd been cashing them all over the neighborhood. (MAMA *stands quite still, without answering.*) How much did he owe you? Plenty, I'll bet. (*Still no answer*) Eh? Marta, I said I bet he owed you plenty. Didn't he?

MAMA (*looks around, first at* NELS *and then down at the books on the table. She touches them.*) No. No, he owed us nothing. (*She takes the check from* PAPA, *tearing it.*) Nothing.

JENNY (*persistently*). How much was that check for? (*She reaches her hand for it.*)

MAMA (*evading her*). It does not matter. He paid with better things than money. (*She goes to the stove, where she throws the check, watching it burn.*)

JENNY. I told you right in the beginning that you shouldn't trust him. But you were so sure . . . just like you always are. Mr. Hyde was a gentleman. A gentleman! I bet it must have been a hundred dollars that he rooked you of. Wasn't it?

MAMA (*returning*). Jenny, I cannot talk now. Maybe you don't have things to do. I have.

JENNY (*sneeringly*). What? What have *you* got to do that is so important?

MAMA (*taking up the medicine bottle*). I have to chloroform a cat! (JENNY *steps back in momentary alarm, as if* MAMA *were talking about her, as she goes out into the pantry with the medicine bottle. Blackout. The curtains close. After a moment, the curtains part again on the kitchen, the next morning. The books have been taken off the table, and* MAMA *is setting the breakfast dishes, with* PAPA *helping her.* DAGMAR *comes bursting into the room, back left.*)

DAGMAR. Good morning, Mama. Morning, Papa. Is Uncle Elizabeth better?

MAMA. Dagmar, there is something I must tell you.

DAGMAR. I want to see Uncle Elizabeth first. (*She runs into the pantry.* MAMA *turns helplessly to* PAPA.)

MAMA. Do something! Tell her!

PAPA. If we just let her think the cat die . . . by itself . . .

MAMA. No. We cannot tell her lies. (PAPA *goes to the pantry door, opening it.*)

DAGMAR (*heard in pantry, off*). What a funny smell. Good

morning, my darling, my darling Elizabeth. (MAMA *and* PAPA *stand stricken.* DAGMAR *comes in carrying the cat, wrapped in an old shirt, with its head covered.*) My goodness, you put enough blankets on him! Did you think he'd catch cold?

MAMA (*horror-stricken*). Dagmar, you must not—(*She stops at the sight of the cat, whose tail is twitching, quite obviously alive.*) Dagmar, let me see. Let me see the cat! (*She goes over to her, and uncovers the head.*)

DAGMAR (*overjoyed*). He's well. Oh, Mama I *knew* you'd fix him!

MAMA (*appalled*). But, Dagmar, I didn't. I . . .

DAGMAR (*ignoring her*). I'm going to take him right up and show him to Nels. (*She runs off back left, calling.*) Nels! Nels! Uncle Elizabeth's well again!

MAMA (*turning to* PAPA.) Is a miracle!

PAPA (*shrugging*). You cannot have used enough chloroform. You just give him good sleep, and that cures him.

MAMA. But, Lars we must tell her. Is not *good* to let her grow up believing I can fix *everything!*

PAPA. Is best thing in world for her to believe. (*He chuckles.*) Besides, I know exactly how she feels. (*He lays his hand on hers.*)

MAMA (*turning with embarrassment*). We finish getting breakfast. (*She turns to the table. The curtains close.*)

(*Curtain*)

TALKING ABOUT THE PLAY

1. A major part of the conversation between Mama and Katrin concerns money and riches. How do they differ about the value of money and riches? What do you

think Mama meant when she said she would like to be rich the way she would like to be ten feet high? What does being rich and having a lot of money mean to Katrin? What might an important problem of this family be, as indicated by this conversation?

2. In answer to Dagmar's pleading, Mama promises to "try" to cure Uncle Elizabeth. Is this the best answer she could have given? What else might she have said? At this point, what are Mama's feelings toward Dagmar, toward Papa, and toward the cat? Later, what are Mama's feelings when Dagmar finds the cat recovered? What do these incidents show about Mama's personality?

3. What do you understand about Mr. Hyde's life with the family during the past few months? What has he contributed? Do you think he deliberately meant to hurt and cheat the family by giving them the worthless check? Why do you think he wrote bad checks? In what ways is he a good or evil man?

4. An important point in this play occurs when Dagmar tells Mama she knew Mama would cure the cat. This high point of feeling and excitement is called the climax. How does Mama act and feel at this moment? How does this event affect Papa? Why does Papa prevent Mama from telling Dagmar the truth?

5. How does the playwright indicate before the play starts that Mama is the central character? Cite examples of conversation in the play that further emphasize Mama's importance.

6. Mr. Hyde and Aunt Jenny are minor characters, but they do contribute to the development of the play. What did you learn about Mama's personality by observing her contacts with them? Did Mr. Hyde and Aunt Jenny help you understand better any other people or ideas in the play?

7. This one-act play is an excerpt (a selected part) of a complete three-act play with the same title and characters. The action in this play moves quickly from one scene to another. What are the different scenes or incidents that are presented in this excerpt? How can the changes from one scene to another be done smoothly on the stage? What particular characters, ideas, or actions continue through the different incidents and give unity to the play?

FOR YOUR OWN WRITING

1. The play title "I Remember Mama" should bring to mind pleasant memories of people you remember. Write a personal sketch entitled "I Remember _____." You may write about an unforgettable real-life person you have known, or you could use your imagination and pretend you remember some famous person in history, science, sports, literature, etc.

2. In this play, Katrin is very concerned about growing up. She wants to be "rich and famous" and to buy beautiful clothes and jewelry for her mother. Do you think she is wise in her ambitions? Would you, too, seek wealth and fame, or do you have other goals that you think are more important or more realistic? Write a composition about your goals.

3. Do you agree with Mama that being rich would be "good for some things—bad for others"? Write a composition telling of particular ways in which money would be helpful or harmful.

4. When the cat gets well, Dagmar seems to believe that Mama can "fix everything." Do you agree with Papa that it is good for children to have such confidence in adults? In what ways is it good to have older relatives or friends whom you can trust and depend on? Or have you known

of a situation in which a young person could not depend on an older one, but had to think and act for himself? Write a composition telling your opinions or your memories.

5. The books Mr. Hyde leaves behind tell us he was well read and scholarly. Pretend you are the playwright and choose different books for Mr. Hyde to leave behind. Write a composition listing your choices and the reasons for your choices. Tell how these changes might or might not change the character of Mr. Hyde.

IN
THE
FOG

MILTON GEIGER

IN THE FOG

Have you ever made a quick judgment about a person, and then discovered that you had been entirely wrong? When you made the discovery, you may have felt pleased, discouraged, or scared—or you may have had a whole mixture of feelings!

In the television play *In the Fog*, the Doctor at first is repelled and frightened by the strangers he has met. But there are feelings of sympathy, which don't quite fit. These feelings are puzzling.

If you are alert, you may find clues that the Doctor missed. To follow the play, though, you will need to understand some television terms. For example, "fade in" and "fade out" can call for the gradual appearing and disappearing of pictures as well as sounds. "Cut to" calls for a sudden change to the shot described, while "dissolve to" requires a slower change. When a camera "dollies in," it moves closer to its subject.

If you follow the action and the camera cues, you may find yourself at first curious, and then scared or shocked. If something seems slightly unusual or unbelievable, don't worry. Let yourself go. Be scared, be shocked—and enjoy it! Follow the Doctor, in this play, as he discovers a truth that he can't quite understand. Can you understand it? Or is it beyond anyone's understanding?

CHARACTERS

THE DOCTOR

ZEKE

EBEN

FILLING STATION ATTENDANT

(SETS: *A signpost on Pennsylvania Route 30. A rock or stump in the fog. A gas station pump.*)

(FADE IN: *Exterior. Night. At first we can only see fog drifting across a dark scene devoid of detail. Then, to weird minor music, the camera dollies in slowly so that out of the fog there emerges toward us a white roadside signpost with a number of white painted signboards pointing to right and to left. The camera continues to dolly in until it has in close-up the state route marker fastened below the signs on the post. The marker is a Pennsylvania State Route—marked characteristically "*PENNA-30.*" Now, a light as from a far headlight sweeps the signs.*)

(SOUND: *Automobile approaching on road. The car pulls up close. We hear the car door open and slam and a man's footsteps approaching on the concrete. Now the signs are lit up again by a more localized, smaller source of light. The light grows stronger as the man, off-stage, approaches. The* DOCTOR *enters the shot, holding a flashlight before him. He scrutinizes*) *the road marker. He flashes his light up at the arrows, the camera moving up with the light. We see the legends on the markers. Pointing off right there are markers that read: York, Columbia, Lancaster; pointing left the signs read: Fayetteville, McConnellsburg, Pennsylvania Turnpike.)*

(CUT TO: *Another angle. We shoot into the* DOCTOR's *perplexed and annoyed face as he turns his flashlight on a folded road map. He is a bit lost in the fog. Then his flashlight fails him. It goes out!)*

DOCTOR. Darn! (*He fumbles with the flashlight in the gloom. Then a voice is raised to him from off-scene.*)

EBEN (*off-scene, strangely*). Turn around, mister . . . (*The* DOCTOR *turns sharply to stare off-scene. His face is lit by a bobbing light from off-scene.*)

ZEKE (*off-scene*). You don't have to be afraid, mister . . .

(CUT TO: *What* DOCTOR *sees. Two men are slowly approaching out of the fog, grotesque in the distorting gloom. One carries a lantern below his knees. The other holds a heavy rifle of dim manufacture. Their features are utterly indistinct as they approach and the rifleman holds up his gun with quiet threat.*)

(CUT TO: *Group shot, angling past* DOCTOR's *shoulder, at their faces.*)

EBEN. You don't have to be afraid.

DOCTOR (*more indignant than afraid*). So you say! Who are you, man?

EBEN. We don't aim to hurt you none.

DOCTOR. That's reassuring. I'd like to know just what you mean by this? This gun business! Who *are* you?

ZEKE (*mildly*). What's your trade, mister?

DOCTOR. I . . . I'm a doctor. Why?

ZEKE (*to* EBEN). Doctor.

EBEN (*nods; then to* DOCTOR). Yer the man we want.

ZEKE. Ye'll do proper, we're thinkin'.

EBEN. So ye'd better come along, mister.

ZEKE. Aye.

DOCTOR. Why? Has—anyone been hurt?

EBEN. It's for you to say if he's been hurt nigh to the finish.

ZEKE. So we're askin' ye to come along, doctor.

(CUT TO: *Another angle, favoring* DOCTOR. *He looks from one to another in indecision and puzzlement.*)

EBEN. In the name o' mercy.

ZEKE. Aye.

DOCTOR. I want you to understand—I'm not afraid of your gun! I'll go to your man all right. Naturally, I'm a doctor. But I demand to know who you are.

ZEKE (*patiently*). Why not? Raise yer lantern, Eben. . . .

EBEN (*tiredly*). Aye.

(EBEN *lifts his lantern. Its light falls on their faces now and we see that they are terrifying. Matted beards, clotted with blood; crude head bandages, crusty with dirt and dry blood. Their hair, stringy and disheveled. Their faces are lean and hollow-cheeked; their eyes sunken and tragic. The* DOCTOR *is shocked for a moment—then bursts out—*)

DOCTOR. Good Lord!—

ZEKE (*impassively*). That's Eben, I'm Zeke.

DOCTOR. What's happened? Has there been an accident or . . . what?

ZEKE. Mischief's happened, stranger.

EBEN. Mischief enough.

DOCTOR (*looks at rifle at his chest*). There's been gunplay—hasn't there?

ZEKE (*mildly ironic*). Yer tellin' us there's been gunplay!

DOCTOR. And I'm telling you that I'm not at all frightened! It's my duty to report this and report it I will!

ZEKE. Aye, mister. You *do* that.

DOCTOR. You're arrogant about it now! You don't think you'll be caught and dealt with. But people are losing patience with you men . . .

(CUT TO: *Close two-shot.* ZEKE *and* EBEN.)

DOCTOR'S VOICE (*off-scene*). . . . You . . . you moonshiners! Running wild . . . a law unto yourselves . . . shooting up the countryside!

ZEKE. Hear that, Eben? Moonshiners.

EBEN. Mischief's happened, mister, we'll warrant that . . .

(*Group shot, favoring* DOCTOR.)

DOCTOR. And I don't like it!

ZEKE. Can't say we like it better'n you do, mister . . .

EBEN (*strangely sad and remote*). What must be, must.

ZEKE. There's no changin' or goin' back and all 'at's left is the wishin' things were different.

EBEN. Aye.

DOCTOR. And while we talk your wounded man lies bleeding I suppose—worthless though he may be. Well? I'll have to get my instrument bag, you know. (*Nods off-scene*) It's in the car.

(EBEN *and* ZEKE *part to let* DOCTOR *pass between them.* DOCTOR *leaves shot grimly as they watch him, off-scene.*)

(SOUND: *Car door opens off-scene. Pause. Slams.*)

(*The* DOCTOR *re-enters the shot, carrying his medical bag.*)

DOCTOR. I'm ready. Lead the way.

(EBEN *lifts his lantern a bit and goes first.* ZEKE *prods the* DOCTOR *ever so gently and apologetically but firmly with the rifle muzzle. The* DOCTOR *leaves the shot next.* ZEKE *strides off slowly after them.*)

(DISSOLVE TO: *Exterior, night. Medium shot of a wounded man lying against a section of stone fence or a boulder or a tree trunk. He, too, is bearded though very young and wears some sort of unidentifiable tunic like the other 'men. His shirt is dark with blood. He breathes stertorously but never stirs otherwise. The light of* EBEN's *bull's-eye falls on him, bobbingly.* EBEN *enters the shot followed by the* DOCTOR *and* ZEKE.

(SOUND: *Owl, far off, from time to time.*)

ZEKE. Ain't stirred a mite since we left 'im.

DOCTOR. Let's have that lantern here! (*The* DOCTOR *tears the man's shirt for better access to the wound.*)

(CLOSE UP: DOCTOR's *face. Appalled.*)

DOCTOR (*softly*). Dreadful! Dreadful . . . !

ZEKE'S VOICE (*off-scene*). Reckon it's bad in the chest like that, hey?

DOCTOR (*taking pulse*). His pulse is positively racing . . . !
    (*Tight group shot.*)

DOCTOR. How long has he been this way?

ZEKE. A long time, mister. A *long* time . . .

DOCTOR (*to* EBEN). You! Hand me my bag.
    (EBEN *puts down lantern and hands bag to* DOCTOR. *The* DOCTOR *opens bag and takes out a couple of retractors.* ZEKE *holds lantern close now.*)

DOCTOR. Lend me a hand with these retractors. (*He works on man, hiding wound from camera with his body.*) All right . . . when I tell you to draw back on the retractors—draw back.

EBEN. Aye.

ZEKE. How is 'e, mister?

DOCTOR (*preoccupied*). More retraction. Pull them a bit more. Hold it. . . .

EBEN. Bad, ain't he?

DOCTOR. Bad enough. The bullet didn't touch any lung tissue far as I can see right now. There's some pneumothorax though. All I can do now is plug the wound. There's some cotton and gauze wadding in my bag. Find it . . .

(ZEKE *probes about silently in the bag and comes up with a small dark box of gauze.*)

DOCTOR. That's it. (*Works a moment in silence.*) I've never seen anything quite like it.

EBEN. Yer young, doctor. Lots o' things you've never seen.

DOCTOR. Adhesive tape!

(ZEKE *finds a roll of three-inch tape and hands it to the* DOCTOR *who tears off long strips and, unseen to camera, slaps them on the dressing and pats and smooths them to man's chest.* EBEN *replaces equipment in* DOCTOR's *bag and closes it with a hint of the finality to come. A preview of dismissal so to speak.*)

DOCTOR (*at length*). There. So much for that. Now then— (*Takes man's shoulders.*) Give me a hand here.

ZEKE (*quiet suspicion*). What fer?

DOCTOR. We've got to move this man.

ZEKE. What fer?

DOCTOR (*stands; indignantly*). We've got to get him to a hospital for treatment; a thorough cleansing of the wound; irrigation. I've done all I can for him here.

ZEKE. I reckon he'll be all right, 'thout no hospital.

DOCTOR. Do you realize how badly this man's hurt!

EBEN. He won't bleed to death, will he?

DOCTOR. I don't think so—not with that plug and pressure dressing. But bleeding isn't the only danger we've got to—

ZEKE (*interrupts*). All right, then. Much obliged to you.

DOCTOR. This man's *dangerously* hurt!

ZEKE. Reckon he'll pull through now, thanks to you.

DOCTOR. I'm glad you feel that way about it! But I'm going to report this to the Pennsylvania State Police at the first telephone I reach!

ZEKE. We ain't stoppin' ye, mister.

EBEN. Fog is liftin', Zeke. Better be done with this, I say.

ZEKE (*nods, sadly*). Aye. Ye can go now, mister . . . and thanks.

(*Group shot. Another angle, favoring* ZEKE, *then* EBEN.)

ZEKE (*continued*). We never meant a mite o' harm, I can tell ye. If we killed, it was no wish of ours.

EBEN. What's done is done. Aye.

ZEKE. Ye can go now, stranger . . .

(EBEN *hands* ZEKE *the* DOCTOR's *bag.* ZEKE *hands it gently to the* DOCTOR.)

DOCTOR. Very well. You haven't heard the last of this, though!

ZEKE. That's the truth, mister. We've killed, aye; and we've been hurt for it . . .

EBEN. Hurt bad.

(*Group shot. Another angle, favoring* DOCTOR *in close shot. His face puckered with doubt and strange apprehension.*)

ZEKE. We're not alone, mister. We ain't the only ones. (*Sighs.*) Ye can go now, doctor . . . and our thanks to ye . . .

(*The camera moves with the* DOCTOR *as he leaves the other two, still gazing at them in strange enchantment and wonder and a touch of indignation. Camera takes his body from waist up as he walks against neutral, featureless background wreathed with some tendrils of fog.*)

EBEN's VOICE (*off-scene*). Thanks, mister . . .

ZEKE's VOICE. In the name o' mercy . . . We thank you . . .

(CUT TO: *Close up:* ZEKE *and* EBEN, *their faces grizzled like the faces of monuments in the park in winter; their eyes unhappy and suffering. The fog drifting across them.*)

EBEN. In the name o' mercy.

ZEKE. Thanks, mister . . .

EBEN. In the name o' kindness . . .

(*The camera pulls back for a group shot of the two men standing; their wounded comrade at their feet—like a group statue in the park . . . grizzled and time-worn. The fog thickens across the scene.*)

(MUSIC: *Eerie, sad.*)

(SOUND: *Far off the long, sad wail of a locomotive whimpers in the dark. Then fades.*)

(FADE OUT.)

(FADE IN: *The illuminated translucent glass globe atop a gasoline pump. The camera pulls back to show the young* ATTENDANT *standing in front of the pump taking a reading and recording it in a book as he prepares to close up. Lights sweep him. He turns as he hears the car approach on the gravel drive.*)

(SOUND: *Car approaching. Crunches on gravel and stops. Door opens and slams off.* DOCTOR'S *feet crunch on gravel, approaching swiftly.*)

(DOCTOR *enters shot.*)

ATTENDANT (*pleasantly*). Good evening, sir. (*Nods off at off-scene car.*) Care to pull 'er up to this pump, sir? Closing up.

DOCTOR (*impatiently*). No. Where's your telephone, please? I've just been held up!

ATTENDANT. Pay-station inside, sir . . .

DOCTOR. ·Thank you! (*The* DOCTOR *starts to go past the* ATTENDANT.)

ATTENDANT. Excuse me, sir . . .

DOCTOR (*stops*). Eh, what is it, what is it?

ATTENDANT. Uh . . . what sort of looking fellows were they?

DOCTOR. Oh—two big fellows with a rifle; faces and heads bandaged and smeared with dirt and blood. Friend of theirs with a gaping hole in his chest. I'm a doctor so they forced me to attend him. Why?

ATTENDANT. *Those* fellers, huh?

DOCTOR. Then you know about them!

ATTENDANT. I guess so.

DOCTOR. They're armed and they're desperate!

ATTENDANT. That was about two or three miles back, would you say?

DOCTOR (*fumbling in pocket*). Just about—I don't seem to have the change. I wonder if you'd spare me change for a quarter . . . ?

ATTENDANT (*makes change from metal coin cannister at his belt*). Certainly, sir . . .

DOCTOR. What town was that back there, now?

ATTENDANT (*dumps coins in other's hand*). There you are, sir.

DOCTOR (*impatient*). Yes, thank you. I say—what town was that back there, so I can tell the police?

(*Two shot. A new angle favoring* ATTENDANT. *His eyes are serious and candid; matter-of-fact and very steady.*)

ATTENDANT. That was . . . Gettysburg, mister . . .

(MUSIC: *Softly. Eerily poignant.* "*Dixie*" *and* "*Battle Hymn of the Republic*" *in minor counterpoint.*)

(*Camera slowly trucks around for two shot that slowly favors* DOCTOR.)

DOCTOR. Gettysburg . . . ?

ATTENDANT. Gettysburg and Gettysburg battlefield . . .
(*Looks off.*) When it's light and the fog's gone, you can

see the gravestones. Meade's men . . . Pickett's men, Robert E. Lee's. . . .

(*The* DOCTOR *is looking off with the* ATTENDANT; *now he turns his head slowly to stare at the other man.*)

ATTENDANT (*continues*). On nights like this—well—you're not the first those men've stopped . . . or the last. (*Nods off.*) Fill 'er up, mister?

(*Camera dollies in slowly on the rapt face of the* DOCTOR.)

DOCTOR. Yes, fill 'er up . . .

(FADE OUT.)

(MUSIC FINISHES.)

TALKING ABOUT THE PLAY

1. As the play begins, the Doctor acts annoyed. How do his feelings change as the two strangers approach? What are the Doctor's first thoughts as to the identity of the strangers? What does he think happened to them? Were your first judgments of the strangers the same as the Doctor's judgments? Toward the end of the play, how do his ideas change?

2. Do you think Zeke and Eben are real people or supernatural beings? Or are they something the Doctor imagines? What happens to a person's imagination, sometimes, during a thick fog? What facts or statements in the play might you discuss to prove that the strangers are *not* something the Doctor has imagined?

3. As the Doctor takes care of the wounded man, he remarks, "I've never seen anything quite like it." Eben answers, "Lots of things you've never seen." What does Eben mean? What happened at Gettysburg that will help you understand what Eben meant? Which of the

men's other statements gain new and deeper meanings when you learn the men's true place and occupation? What might the Doctor have learned if he had paid more attention to their remarks, or asked more questions?

4. What does the gas station attendant seem to know about the strangers in the fog? What is his attitude toward them?

5. Did the title of the play give you any clues to the plot? Why do you think the playwright used this simple title? What other titles could you suggest for the play?

6. This play was written for television. How do the directions for the camera, set, actions, and sounds all help to build suspense and create the mood? Why are these directions particularly suitable for television rather than for a stage play, a movie, or radio?

FOR YOUR OWN WRITING

1. Think of the different people or ghosts who might haunt different particular places. Then imagine you are lost in such a place, in a heavy fog, and you meet some strangers. Write a story or play about your experience, describing when and where you were lost, whom you met, and what happened.

2. Suppose the Doctor had really called the police. Pretend that you are one of the policemen. Write the report that the policeman might have written, after the incident, for his captain at the station. Or, you might want to write a TV or radio script showing the scene between the policeman and the doctor.

3. Pretend you are a resident in the Gettysburg countryside. What different adventures with the strangers might you have? Write an account of such an adventure.

4. What kind of men might Zeke and Eben have been before the war? Where were their homes? Who were their relatives and friends? Can you write a short biography of one of them? Or, you could write the dramatic scene in which one of them leaves his home to go to the war.

THE
BIG
WAVE

PEARL BUCK

THE BIG WAVE

What is the farthest you have ever traveled?

Through plays, movies, and TV, you can see other lands and people right before your eyes. In *The Big Wave*, you will meet two Japanese boys as they face tragedy, excitement, and decisions. Their lives are different from ours in many small ways, but their deepest problems and attitudes are common to us and to all mankind.

This TV drama couldn't be broadcast completely "live" from a studio; it would have to be filmed. The Japanese landscape scenes, for example, would be filmed outside, and then edited and skillfully put together. Thus the "montage," or rapid sequence of scenes, can show the countryside at the beginning of the first two acts. But one problem arises: it's unlikely that the cameramen could find a real earthquake and tidal wave to photograph just when they needed a picture! Here, they might splice in clips from a newsreel film of a real wave. Or, they might create their own wave in the studio, by making a miniature town and splashing a small wave over it.

The narrator of this play serves special purposes. He gives information about the people and their country. He expresses important ideas about the meaning of life. He indicates the passage of time. And he describes other things which the camera cannot catch completely, such as Jiya's feelings and the effects of the wave.

This TV drama is divided into five acts. Besides showing the passage of time and providing a break for the viewer, these divisions have a very practical purpose. (What happens on TV during breaks in the play or movie?)

Meet Kino and Jiya, and watch them grow up. Experience the big wave with them, and learn with them about life.

CHARACTERS

NARRATOR

KINO UCHIYAMA, a farmer's son

MOTHER

FATHER, the farmer

SETSU, Kino's sister

JIYA, a fisherman's son

JIYA'S FATHER, the fisherman

OLD GENTLEMAN, a wealthy landowner

TWO MEN SERVANTS

GARDENER

FIRST MAN

SECOND MAN

WOMAN

CHILD

Act 1

(*A scene in Japan, sea and mountainside, and in the distance Mount Fuji.*)

(DISSOLVE TO: *A small farmhouse, built on top of the terraces. This, as the* NARRATOR *speaks, dissolves to the inside of the house, a room with the simplest of Japanese furniture.*)

NARRATOR. Kino lives on a farm. The farm lies on the side of a mountain in Japan. The fields are terraced by walls of stone, each one of them like a broad step up the mountain. Centuries ago, Kino's ancestors built the stone walls that hold up the fields. Above the fields stands this farmhouse, which is Kino's home. Sometimes he feels the climb is hard, especially when he has been working in the lowest field and is hungry.

(DISSOLVE TO: KINO *comes into the room. He is a sturdy boy of about thirteen, dressed in shorts, and a Japanese jacket, open on his bare chest.*)

(MOTHER *hurries in. She is a small, serious-looking woman*

dressed in an everyday cotton kimono, sleeves tucked up. She is carrying a jar of water.)

MOTHER. Dinner is ready. Where is your father?

KINO. Coming. I ran up the terrace, I'm starving.

MOTHER. Call Setsu. She is playing outside.

KINO (*turning his head*). Setsu!

FATHER. Here she is. (*He comes in, holding by the hand a small roguish girl.*) Getting so big! I can't lift her anymore. (*But he does lift her so high that she touches the rafters.*)

SETSU. Don't put me down, I want to eat my supper up here.

FATHER. And fall into the soup?

KINO. How would that taste?

SETSU (*willfully*). It would taste nice.

MOTHER. Come, come— (*They sit on the floor around the little table. The* MOTHER *serves swiftly from a small bucket of rice, a bowl of soup, a bowl of fish. She serves the* FATHER *first, then* KINO, *then* SETSU, *then herself.*)

FATHER. Kino, don't eat so fast.

KINO. I have promised Jiya to swim in the sea with him.

MOTHER. Obey your father.

FATHER (*smiling*). Let him eat fast. (*He puts a bit of fish in* SETSU's *bowl.*) There—that's a good bit.

KINO. Father, why is it that Jiya's father's house has no window to the sea?

FATHER. No fisherman wants windows to the sea.

MOTHER. The sea is their enemy.

KINO. Mother, how can you say so? Jiya's father catches fish from the sea and that is how his family lives.

FATHER. Do not argue with your mother. Ask Jiya your question. See what he says.

KINO. Then may I go?

FATHER. Go.

(MONTAGE: *Film. A sandy strip of seashore at the foot of the mountain. A few cottages stand there.* DISSOLVE TO: JIYA, *a tall slender boy. He stands at the edge of the sea, looking up the mountain.*)

JIYA (*calling through his hands*). Kino!

KINO. Coming. (*He is running and catches* JIYA's *outstretched hand, so that they nearly fall down. They laugh and throw off their jackets.*)

KINO. Wait—I am out of breath. I ate too much.

JIYA (*looking up the mountain*). There's Old Gentleman standing at the gate of his castle.

KINO. He is watching to see whether we are going to the sea.

JIYA. He's always looking at the sea—at dawn, at sunset.

(DISSOLVE TO: OLD GENTLEMAN, *standing on the rock, in front of his castle, halfway up the mountain. The wind is blowing his beard. He wears the garments of an aristocrat. Withdraw the cameras to the beach again.*)

JIYA. He is afraid of the sea—always watching!

KINO. Have you ever been in his castle?

JIYA. Only once. Such beautiful gardens—like a dream in a fairy tale. The old pines are bent with the wind, and under them the moss is deep and green and so smooth. Every day men sweep the moss with brooms.

KINO. Why does he keep looking to the sea?

JIYA. He is afraid of it. I tell you.

KINO. Why?

JIYA. The sea is our enemy. We all know it.

KINO. Oh, how can you say it? When we have so much fun . . .

JIYA. It is our enemy . . .

KINO. Not mine—let's swim to the island.

JIYA. No. I must find clams for my mother.

KINO. Then let's swim to the sandbar. There are millions of clams there.

JIYA. But the tide is ready to turn . . .

KINO. It's slow—we'll have time.

(*They plunge into the sea and swim to the sandbar.* JIYA *has a small, short-handled hoe hanging from his girdle. He digs into the sand.* KINO *kneels to help him. But* JIYA *digs for only a moment; then he pauses to look out over the sea.*)

KINO. What are you looking for?

JIYA. To see if the sea is angry with us.

KINO (*laughing*). Silly—the sea can't be angry with people.

JIYA. Down there, a mile down, the old sea god lives. When he is angry he heaves and rolls, and the waves rush back and forth. Then he gets up and stamps his foot, and the earth shakes at the bottom of the sea . . . I wish I were a farmer's son, like you . . .

KINO. And I wish I were a fisherman's son. It is stupid to plow and plant and cut sheaves, when I could just sit in a boat and reap fish from the sea!

JIYA. The earth is safe.

KINO. When the volcano is angry the earth shakes too.

JIYA. The angry earth helps the angry sea.

KINO. They work together.

JIYA. But fire comes out of the volcano.

(*Meanwhile, the tide is coming in and swirls about their feet.*)

JIYA (*noticing*). Oh—we have not half enough clams . . .

(*They fall to digging fanatically.*)

(DISSOLVE TO: *The empty seashore and the tide rushing in. A man paces the sand at the water's edge. He wears shorts and a fisherman's jacket, open above his bare breast. He calls, his hands cupped about his mouth.*)

JIYA'S FATHER. Ji————ya!

(*There is only the sound of the surf. He wades into the water, still calling. Suddenly he sees the boys, and he beckons fiercely. They come in, and he gives a hand to each one and pulls them out of the sea.*)

JIYA'S FATHER. Jiya! You have never been so late before.

JIYA. Father, we were on the sand bar, digging clams. We had to leave them.

JIYA'S FATHER (*shaking his shoulders*). Never be so late!

KINO (*wondering*). You are afraid of the sea, too?

JIYA'S FATHER. Go home, farmer's boy. Your mother is calling you.

(*In the distance a woman's voice is calling* KINO's *name. He hears and runs toward the mountain.*)

JIYA. Father, I have made you angry.

JIYA'S FATHER. I am not angry.

JIYA. Then why do you seem angry?

JIYA'S FATHER. Old Gentleman sent down word that a storm is rising behind the horizon. He sees the clouds through his great telescope.

JIYA. Father, why do you let Old Gentleman make you afraid? Just because he is rich and lives in a castle, everybody listens to him.

JIYA'S FATHER. Not because he is rich—not because he lives in a castle, but because he is old and wise and he knows the sea. He doesn't want anybody to die. (*He looks over the sea, and his arm tightens about his son, and he mutters as though to himself.*) Though all must die . . .

JIYA. Why must all die, Father?

JIYA'S FATHER. Who knows? Simply, it is so.

(*They stand looking over the sea.*)

(MONTAGE. *Film of the Japanese scene as in Act 1.*)

NARRATOR. Yet there was much in life to enjoy. Kino had a good time every day. In the winter he went to school in the fishing village, and he and Jiya shared a bench and writing table. They studied reading and arithmetic and learned what all children must learn in school. But in the summer Kino had to work hard on the farm. Even Setsu and the mother had to help when the rice seedlings were planted in the watery terraced fields. On those days Kino could not run down the mountainside to find Jiya. When the day was ended he was so tired he fell asleep over his supper.

There were days when Jiya, too, could not play. Schools of fish came into the channel between the shore and the island, and early in the morning Jiya and his father sailed their boats out to sea to cast their nets at dawn. If they were lucky, their nets came up so heavy with fish that it took all their strength to haul them in, and soon the bottom of the boat was flashing and sparkling with wriggling fish.

Sometimes, if it were not seedtime or harvest, Kino went with Jiya and his father. It was exciting to get up in the night and put on his warm padded jacket; for even in summer the wind was cool over the sea at dawn. However early he got up, his mother was up even earlier to give him a bowl of hot rice soup and some bean curd and tea before he went. She packed for him a lunch in a clean little wooden box—cold rice and fish and a radish pickle. Down the stone steps of the mountain path, Kino ran straight to the narrow dock where the fishing boats bobbed up and down with the tide. Jiya and his father were already there, and in a few minutes their boat was nosing its way past the sandbar toward the open sea. Sails set, and filling with wind, they sped straight into the dawnlit horizon. Kino crouched down in the bow, and his heart rose with joy and excitement. It was like flying into the sky. The winds were so mild, the sea lay so calm and blue, that it was hard to believe that it could be cruel and angry. Actually it was the earth that brought the big wave.

One day, as Kino helped his father plant turnips, a cloud came over the sun.

(DISSOLVE TO: *A field, and* KINO *and his* FATHER. *The volcano is in the background.*)

KINO. Look, Father, the volcano is burning again!

FATHER (*straightens and gazes anxiously at the sky*). It looks very angry. I shall not sleep tonight. We must hurry home.

KINO. Why should the volcano be angry, Father?

FATHER. Who knows? Simply, the inner fire burns. Come—make haste.

(*They gather their tools.*)

(DISSOLVE TO: *Night. The threshing floor outside the farmhouse.* KINO'S FATHER *sits on a bench outside the door. He gets up and walks to and fro and gazes at the red sky above the volcano. The* MOTHER *comes to the door.*)

MOTHER. Can you put out the volcano by not sleeping?

FATHER. Look at the fishing village! Every house is lit. And the lamps are lit in the castle. Shall I sleep like a fool?

MOTHER. I have taken the dishes from the shelves and put away our good clothes in boxes.

FATHER (*gazing down at the village*). If only I knew whether it would be earth or sea. Both work evil together. The fires rage under the sea, the rocks boil. The volcano is vent unless the sea bottom breaks.

KINO (*coming to the door*). Shall we have an earthquake, Father?

FATHER. I cannot tell.

MOTHER. How still it is. There's no wind. The sea is purple.

KINO. Why is the sea such a color?

FATHER. Sea mirrors sky. Sea and earth and sky—if they work against man, who can live?

KINO (*coming to his* FATHER's *side*). Where are the gods? Do they forget us?

FATHER. There are times when the gods leave men alone. They test us to see how able we are to save ourselves.

KINO. What if we are not able?

FATHER. We must be able. Fear makes us weak. If you are afraid, your hands tremble, your feet falter. Brain cannot tell hands what to do.

SETSU (*her voice calling from inside the house*). Mother, I'm afraid!

MOTHER. I am coming. (*She goes away.*)

FATHER. The sky is growing black. Go into the house, Kino.

KINO. Let me stay with you.

FATHER. The red flag is flying over the castle. Twice I've seen that red flag go up, both times before you were born. Old Gentleman wants everybody to be ready.

KINO (*frightened*). Ready for what?

FATHER. For whatever must be.

(*A deep-toned bell tolls over the mountainside.*)

KINO. What is that bell? I've never heard it before.

FATHER. It rang twice before you were born. It is the bell inside Old Gentleman's temple. He is calling to the people to come up out of the village and shelter within his walls.

KINO. Will they come?

FATHER. Not all of them. Parents will try to make their children go, but the children will not want to leave their parents. Mothers will not want to leave fathers, and the fathers will stay by the boats. But some will want to be sure of life.

(*The bell continues to ring urgently. Soon from the village comes a straggling line of people, nearly all of them children.*)

KINO (*gazing at them*). I wish Jiya would come. (*He takes off his white cloth girdle and waves it.*)

(DISSOLVE TO: JIYA *and his* FATHER *by their house. Sea in the background, roaring.*)

JIYA'S FATHER. Jiya, you must go to the castle.

JIYA. I won't leave you and mother.

JIYA'S FATHER. We must divide ourselves. If we die, you must live after us.

JIYA. I don't want to live alone.

JIYA'S FATHER. It is your duty to obey me, as a good Japanese son.

JIYA. Let me go to Kino's house.

JIYA'S FATHER. Only go—go quickly.

(JIYA *and his* FATHER *embrace fiercely, and* JIYA *runs away, crying, to leap up to the mountainside.*)

(DISSOLVE TO: *Terrace and farmhouse, and center on* KINO *and his* FATHER, *who put out their hands to help* JIYA *up the last terrace. Suddenly* KINO *screams.*)

KINO. Look—look at the sea!

FATHER. May the gods save us.

(*The bell begins to toll, deep, pleading, incessant.*)

JIYA (*shrieking*). I must go back—I must tell my father . . .

FATHER (*holding him*). It is too late . . .

(FILM. *The sea rushes up in a terrible wave and swallows the shore. The water roars about the foot of the mountain.*)
(JIYA, *held by* KINO *and his* FATHER, *stares transfixed, and then sinks unconscious to the ground. The bell tolls on.*)

Act 3

NARRATOR. So the big wave came, swelling out of the sea. It lifted the horizon while the people watched. The air was filled with its roar and shout. It rushed over the flat, still waters of the sea; it reached the village and covered it fathoms deep in swirling, wild water—green, laced with fierce white foam. The wave ran up the mountainside until the knoll upon which the castle stood was an island. All who were still climbing the path were swept away, mere tossing scraps in the wicked waters. Then with a great sucking sigh, the wave ebbed into the sea, dragging everything with it—trees, rocks, houses, people. Once again it swept over the village, and once again it returned to the sea, sinking into great stillness.

Upon the beach, where the village stood, not a house remained, no wreckage of wood or fallen stone wall, no street of little shops, no docks, not a single boat. The beach was as clean as if no human being had ever lived there. All that had been was now no more.

(DISSOLVE TO: *Inside the farmhouse. The farm family is gathered about the mattress on which* JIYA *lies.*)
MOTHER. This is not sleep. . . . Is it death?
FATHER. Jiya is not dead. His soul has withdrawn for a time. He is unconscious. Let him remain so until his own will wakes him.
MOTHER (*rubbing* JIYA's *hands and feet*). Kino, do not cry.

(KINO *cannot stop crying, although silently.*)

FATHER. Let him cry. Tears comfort the heart. (*He feels* KINO's *hands and cheeks.*) He is cold. Heat a little rice soup for him and put some ginger in it. I will stay with Jiya.

(MOTHER *goes out.* SETSU *comes in, rubbing her eyes and yawning.*)

FATHER. Sleepy eyes! You have slept all through the storm. Wise one!

SETSU (*coming to stare at* JIYA). Is Jiya dead?

FATHER. No, Jiya is living.

SETSU. Why doesn't he open his eyes?

FATHER. Soon he will open his eyes.

SETSU. If Jiya is not dead, why does Kino stand there crying?

FATHER. As usual, you are asking too many questions. Go back to the kitchen and help your mother.

(SETSU *goes out, staring and sucking her thumb.* FATHER *puts his arm around* KINO.)

FATHER. The first sorrow is the hardest to bear.

KINO. What will we say to Jiya when he wakes? How can we tell him?

FATHER. We will not talk. We will give him warm food and let him rest. We will help him to feel he still has a home.

KINO. Here?

FATHER. Here. I have always wanted another son, and Jiya will be that son. As soon as he knows this is his home, we must help him to understand what has happened. Ah, here is Mother, with your hot rice soup. Eat it, my son—food for the body is food for the heart, sometimes.

(KINO *takes the bowl from his* MOTHER *with both hands and drinks. The parents look at each other and at him, sorrowfully and tenderly.* SETSU *comes in and leans her head toward her* MOTHER.)

(DISSOLVE TO: The same room, the same scene except that MOTHER *and* SETSU *are not there.* FATHER *sits beside* JIYA's *bed,* KINO *is at the open door.*)

KINO. The sky is golden, Father, and the sea is smooth. How cruel—

FATHER. No, it is wonderful that after the storm the sea grows calm again, and the sky is clear. It was not the sea or sky that made the evil storm.

KINO (*not turning his head*). Who made it?

FATHER. Ah, no one knows who makes evil storms. (*He takes* JIYA's *hand and rubs it gently.*) We only know that they come. When they come we must live through them as bravely as we can, and after they are gone we must feel again how wonderful life is. Every day of life is more valuable now than it was before the storm.

KINO. But Jiya's father and mother—and the other fisherfolk— so good and kind—all of them—lost. (*He cannot go on.*)

FATHER. We must think of Jiya—who lives. (*He stops,* JIYA *has begun to sob softly in his unconsciousness.*)

FATHER. Quick, Kino—call your mother and Setsu. He will open his eyes at any moment, and we must all be here— you to be his brother, I, his father, and the mother, the sister—

(KINO *runs out,* FATHER *kneels beside* JIYA, *who stirs, still sobbing.* KINO *comes back with* MOTHER *and* SETSU. *They kneel on the floor beside the bed.* JIYA's *eyelids flutter. He opens his eyes and looks from one to the other. He stares at the beams of the roof, the walls of the room, the bed, his own hands. All are quiet except* SETSU, *who cannot keep from laughing. She claps her hands.*)

SETSU. Oh, Jiya has come back. Jiya, did you have a good dream?

JIYA (*faintly*). My father, my mother—

MOTHER (*taking his hands in both hers*). I will be your mother now, dear Jiya.

FATHER. I will be your father.

KINO. I am your brother now, Jiya. (*He falters.*)

SETSU (*joyfully*). Oh, Jiya, you will live with us.

(JIYA *gets up slowly. He walks to the door, goes out, and looks down the hillside.*)

(DISSOLVE TO: *The peaceful empty beach. Then back to the farmhouse and* JIYA, *standing outside and looking at the sea.* SETSU *comes to him.*)

SETSU. I will give you my pet duck. He'll follow you—he'll make you laugh.

MOTHER (*leaving the room*). We ought all to eat something. I have a fine chicken for dinner.

KINO (*coming to* JIYA). Mother makes such good chicken soup.

SETSU. I'm hungry, I tell you.

FATHER. Come, Jiya, my son.

(JIYA *stands still dazed.*)

KINO. Eat with us, Jiya.

JIYA. I am tired—very tired.

KINO. You have been sleeping so long.

JIYA (*slowly*). I shall never see them again. (*He puts his hands over his eyes.*) I shall keep thinking about them— floating in the sea.

MOTHER (*coming in*). Drink this bowl of soup at least, Jiya, my son.

(JIYA *drinks and lets the bowl fall. It is wooden and does not break.*)

JIYA. I want to sleep.

FATHER. Sleep, my son. Sleep is good for you. (*He leads* JIYA *to the bed and covers him with a quilt.*)

FATHER (*to them all*). Jiya is not yet ready to live. We must wait.

KINO. Will he die?

FATHER. Life is stronger than death. He will live.

Act 4

NARRATOR. The body heals first, and the body heals the mind and the soul. Jiya ate food, he got out of bed sometimes, but he was still tired. He did not want to think or remember. He only wanted to sleep. He woke to eat, and then he went to sleep again. In the quiet, clean room Jiya slept, and the mother spread the quilt over him and closed the door and went away.

All through these days Kino did not play about as he once had. He was no longer a child. He worked hard beside his father in the fields. They did not talk much, and neither of them wanted to look at the sea. It was enough to look at the earth, dark and rich beneath their feet.

One evening Kino climbed the mountain behind the house and looked up at the volcano. The heavy cloud of smoke had gone away, and the sky was clear. He was glad that the volcano was no longer angry, and he went down again to the house. On the threshold his father was smoking his usual evening pipe. In the house his mother was giving Setsu her evening bath.

KINO (*dropping down on the bench beside his father*). Is Jiya asleep, again?

FATHER. Yes, and it is a good thing for him. When he sleeps enough, he will wake and remember.

KINO. But should he remember?

FATHER. Only when he dares to remember his parents will he be happy again. (*A silence*)

KINO. Father, are we are not very unfortunate people to live in Japan?

FATHER. Why do you think so?

KINO. The volcano is behind our house and the sea is in front. When they work together to make earthquake and big wave, we are helpless. Always, many of us are lost.

FATHER. To live in the presence of death makes us brave and strong. That is why our people never fear death. We see it too often, and we do not fear it. To die a little sooner or a little later does not matter. But to live bravely, to love life, to see how the beautiful trees are and the mountains—yes, and even the sea—to enjoy work because it produces food—in these ways we are fortunate people. We love life because we live in danger. We do not fear death, for we understand that death and life are necessary to each other.

KINO. What is death?

FATHER. Death is the great gateway.

KINO. The gateway—where?

FATHER. Can you remember when you were born?

KINO. I was too small.

FATHER (*smiling*). I remember very well. Oh, hard you thought it was to be born. You cried and you screamed.

KINO (*much interested*). Didn't I want to be born?

FATHER. You did not. You wanted to stay just where you were, in the warm dark house of the unborn, but the time came to be born, and the gate of life opened.

KINO. Did I know it was the gate of life?

FATHER. You did not know anything about it, and so you were afraid. But see how foolish you were! Here we were waiting for you, your parents, already loving you and eager to welcome you. And you have been very happy, haven't you?

KINO. Until the big wave came. Now I am afraid again because of the death the big wave brought.

FATHER. You are only afraid because you don't know anything about death. But someday you will wonder why you were afraid, even as today you wonder why you once feared to be born.

KINO. I think I understand—I begin to understand . . .

FATHER. Do not hurry yourself. You have plenty of time. (*He rises to his feet.*) Now what do I see? A lantern coming up the hill.

KINO (*running to the edge of the threshold*). Who can be coming now? It is almost night.

FATHER. A visitor—ah, why, it's Old Gentleman!

(OLD GENTLEMAN *indeed is climbing the hill. He is somewhat breathless in spite of his long staff. His* MANSERVANT *carries the lantern, and, when they arrive, steps to one side.*)

OLD GENTLEMAN (*to* MANSERVANT). Is this the house of Uchiyama, the farmer?

MANSERVANT. It is—and this is the farmer himself and his son.

FATHER (*bowing deeply*). Please, Honored Sir, what can I do for you?

OLD GENTLEMAN. Do you have a lad here by the name of Jiya?

FATHER. He lies sleeping in my house.

OLD GENTLEMAN. I wish to see him.

FATHER. Sir, he suffered the loss of his parents when the big wave came. Now sleep heals him.

OLD GENTLEMAN. I will not wake him. I only wish to look at him.

FATHER. Please come in.

(DISSOLVE TO: JIYA *asleep. The* MANSERVANT *holds the lantern so that the light does not fall on* JIYA's *face directly.* OLD GENTLEMAN *looks at him carefully.*)

OLD GENTLEMAN. Tall and strong for his age—intelligent—handsome. Hm--yes. (*He motions to the* MANSERVANT *to lead him away, and the scene returns to the dooryard.*)

OLD GENTLEMAN (*to* FATHER). It is my habit, when the big wave comes, to care for those who are orphaned by it. Thrice in my lifetime I have searched out the orphans, and I have fed them and sheltered them. But I have heard of this boy Jiya and wish to do more for him. If he is as good as he is handsome, I will take him for my own son.

KINO. But Jiya is ours!

FATHER (*sternly*). Hush. We are only poor people. If Old Gentleman wants Jiya, we cannot say we will not give him up.

OLD GENTLEMAN. Exactly. I will give him fine clothes and send him to a good school, and he may become a great man and an honor to our whole province and even to the nation.

KINO. But if he lives in the castle we can't be brothers!

FATHER. We must think of Jiya's good. (*He turns to* OLD GENTLEMAN.) Sir, it is very kind of you to propose this for Jiya. I had planned to take him for my own son, now that he has lost both his parents; but I am only a poor farmer, and I cannot pretend that my house is as good as yours or that I can afford to send Jiya to a fine school. Tomorrow when he wakes I will tell him of your fine offer. He will decide.

OLD GENTLEMAN. Very well. But let him come and tell me himself.

FATHER (*proudly*). Certainly. Jiya must speak for himself.

(OLD GENTLEMAN *bows slightly and prepares to depart.*

FATHER *bows deeply and taps* KINO *on the head to make him bow.* OLD GENTLEMAN *and his* MANSERVANT *return down the mountain.*)

KINO. If Jiya goes away, I shall never have a brother.

FATHER. Kino, don't be selfish. You must allow Jiya to make his own choice. It would be wrong to persuade him. I forbid you to speak to him of this matter. When he wakes, I will tell him myself.

KINO (*pleading*). Don't tell him today, Father.

FATHER. I must tell him as soon as he wakes. It would not be fair to Jiya to let him grow used to thinking of this house as his home. He must make the choice today, before he has time to put down his new roots. Go now, Kino, and weed the lower terrace.

(DISSOLVE TO: KINO *working in the terrace, weeding. It is evident that he has worked for some time. He looks hot and dusty, and he has quite a pile of weeds. He stops to look up at the farmhouse, but he sees no one and resigns himself again to his work. Suddenly his name is called.*)

FATHER. Kino!

KINO. Shall I come?

FATHER. No, I'm coming—with Jiya.

(KINO *stands waiting.* FATHER *and* JIYA *come down the terraces.* JIYA *is very sad. When he sees* KINO, *he tries not to cry.*)

FATHER (*putting his arm about* JIYA's *shoulder*). Jiya, you must not mind that you cry easily. Until now you couldn't cry because you weren't fully alive. You had been hurt too much. But today you are beginning to live, and so your tears flow. It is good for you. Let your tears come—don't stop them. (*He turns to* KINO.) I have told Jiya that he must not decide where he will live until he has seen the inside of the castle. He must see all that Old Gentleman can give him. Jiya, you know how our house is—four small rooms, and the kitchen, this farm, upon which we have to work hard for our food. We have only what our hands earn for us. (*He holds out his two workworn hands.*) If you live in the castle, you need never have hands like this.

JIYA. I don't want to live in the castle.

FATHER. You don't know whether you do or not; you have never seen the castle inside. (*He turns to* KINO.) Kino, you are to go with Jiya, and when you reach the castle you must persuade him to stay there for his own sake.

KINO. I will go and wash myself—and put on my good clothes.

FATHER. No—go as you are. You are a farmer's son.

(KINO *and* JIYA *go, reluctantly, and* FATHER *stands looking after them.*)

(DISSOLVE TO: *The mountainside and the two boys nearing the gate of the castle. The gate is open, and inside old* GARDENER *is sweeping moss under pine trees. He sees them.*)

GARDENER. What do you want, boys?

KINO. My father sent us to see the honored Old Gentleman.

GARDENER. Are you the Uchiyama boy?

KINO. Yes, please, and this is Jiya, whom Old Gentleman wishes to come and live here.

GARDENER (*bowing to* JIYA). Follow me, young sir.
(*They follow over a pebbled path under the leaning pine trees. In the distance the sun falls upon a flowering garden and a pool with a waterfall.*)

KINO (*sadly*). How beautiful it is—of course you will want to live here. Who could blame you?
(JIYA *does not answer. He walks with his head held high.*

They come to a great door where a MANSERVANT *bids them to take off their shoes. The* GARDENER *leaves them.*)

MANSERVANT. Follow me.

(*They follow through passageways into a great room decorated in the finest Japanese fashion. In the distance at the end of the room, they see* OLD GENTLEMAN, *sitting beside a small table. Behind him the open panels reveal the garden.* OLD GENTLEMAN *is writing. He holds his brush upright in his hand, and he is carefully painting letters on a scroll, his silver rimmed glasses sliding down his nose. When the two boys approach, the* MANSERVANT *announces them.*)

MANSERVANT. Master, the two boys are here.

OLD GENTLEMAN (*to boys*). Would you like to know what I have been writing?

(JIYA *looks at* KINO, *who is too awed to speak.*)

JIYA. Yes, Honored Sir, if you please.

OLD GENTLEMAN (*taking up the scroll*). It is not my own poem. It is the saying of a wise man of India, but I like it so much that I have painted it on this scroll to hang it there in the alcove where I can see it every day. (*He reads clearly and slowly.*)

> "The children of God are very dear,
> But very queer—
> Very nice, but very narrow."

(*He looks up over his spectacles.*) What do you think of it?

JIYA (*looking at* KINO *who is too shy to speak*). We do not understand it, Sir.

OLD GENTLEMAN (*shaking his head and laughing softly*). Ah, we are all children of God! (*He takes off his spectacles and looks hard at* JIYA.) Well? Will you be my son?

(JIYA, *too embarrassed to speak, bites his lip and looks away, etc.*)

OLD GENTLEMAN. Say yes or no. Either word is not hard to speak.

JIYA. I will say—no. (*He feels this is too harsh, and he smiles apologetically.*) I thank you, sir, but I have a home—on a farm.

KINO (*trying to repress his joy and speaking very solemnly as a consequence.*) Jiya, remember how poor we are.

OLD GENTLEMAN (*smiling, half sad*). They are certainly very poor and here, you know, you would have everything. You can invite this farmboy to come and play, sometimes, if you like. And I am quite willing to give the family some money. It would be suitable as my son for you to help the poor.

JIYA (*suddenly, as though he had not heard*). Where are the others who were saved from the big wave?

OLD GENTLEMAN. Some wanted to go away, and the ones who wanted to stay are out in the back yard with my servants.

JIYA. Why do you not invite them to come into the castle and be your sons and daughters?

OLD GENTLEMAN (*somewhat outraged by this*). Because I don't want them for my sons and daughters. You are a bright, handsome boy. They told me you were the best boy in the village.

JIYA. I am not better than the others. My father was a fisherman.

OLD GENTLEMAN (*taking up his spectacles and brush*). Very well—I will do without a son.

(*The* MANSERVANT *motions to the boys to come away, and they follow.*)

MANSERVANT (*to* JIYA). How foolish you are! Our Old
Gentleman is very kind. You would have everything here.

JIYA. Not everything . . .

KINO. Let's hurry home—let's hurry—hurry—

(*They run down the mountainside and up the hill to
the farmhouse.* SETSU *sees them and comes flying down to
meet them, the sleeves of her bright kimono like wings,
and her feet clattering in their wooden sandals.*)

SETSU. Jiya has come home—Jiya, Jiya—

(JIYA *sees her happy face and opens his arms and gives
her a great hug.*)

Act 5

NARRATOR. Now happiness began to live in Jiya, though
secretly and hidden inside him, in ways he did not understand. The good food warmed him, and his body wel-
comed it. Around him the love of four people who received him for their own glowed like a warm and welcoming fire upon his heart.

Time passed. Eight years. Jiya grew up in the farmhouse to be a tall young man, and Kino grew at his side,
solid and strong, but never as tall as Jiya. Setsu grew too,
from a mischievous child, into a gay, willful, pretty girl.
But time, however long, was split in two parts, the time
before and the time after the big wave. The big wave had
changed everybody's life.

In all these years no one returned to live on the empty
beach. The tides rose and fell, sweeping the sands clear
every day. Storms came and went, but there was never
such a wave as the big one. At last people began to think
that never again would there be such a big wave. The

few fishermen who had listened to the tolling bell from the castle, and were saved with their wives and children, went to other shores to fish and they made new fishing boats. Then, as time passed, they told themselves that no beach was quite as good as the old one. There, they said, the water was deep and great fish came close to shore. They did not need to go far out to sea to find booty.

Jiya and Kino had not often gone to the beach, either. At first they had walked along the empty sands where once the street had been, and Jiya searched for some keepsake from his home that the sea might have washed back to the shore. But nothing was ever found. So the two boys, as they grew to be young men, did not visit the deserted beach. When they went to swim in the sea, they walked across the farm and over another fold of the mountains to the shore.

Yet Jiya had never forgotten his father and mother. He thought of them every day, their faces, their voices, the way his father talked, his mother's smile. The big wave had changed him forever. He did not laugh easily or speak carelessly. In school he had earnestly learned all he could, and now he worked hard on the farm. Now, as a man, he valued deeply everything that was good. Since the big wave had been so cruel, he was never cruel, and he grew kind and gentle. Jiya never spoke of his loneliness. He did not want others to be sad because of his sadness. When he laughed at some mischief of Setsu's, when she teased him, his laughter was wonderful to hear because it was whole and real. And, sometimes, in the morning, he went to the door of the farmhouse and looked at the empty beach below, searching with his eyes as though something might one day come back. One day he did see something . . .

JIYA. Kino, come here! (KINO *comes out, his shoes in his hand.*)

JIYA. Look—is someone building a house on the beach?

KINO. Two men—pounding posts into the sand—

JIYA. And a woman—yes, and even a child.

KINO. They can't be building a house.

JIYA. Let's go and see.

(DISSOLVE TO: *The beach. The two* MEN, JIYA *and* KINO, WOMAN *and* CHILD.)

JIYA (*out of breath*). Are you building a house?

FIRST MAN (*wiping sweat from his face*). Our father used to live here, and we with him. We are two brothers. During these years we have lived in the houses of the castle, and we have fished from other shores. Now we are tired of having no homes of our own. Besides, this is still the best beach for fishing.

KINO. What if the big wave comes again?

SECOND MAN (*shrugging his shoulders*). There was a big wave, too, in our great-grandfather's time. All the houses were swept away. But our grandfather came back. In our father's time there was again the big wave. Now we return.

KINO (*soberly*). What of your children?

(*The* MEN *begin to dig again. The* WOMAN *takes the* CHILD *into her arms and gazes out to the sea. Suddenly there is a sound of a voice calling. All look up the mountain.*)

FIRST MAN. Here comes our Old Gentleman.

SECOND MAN. He's very angry or he wouldn't have left the castle. (*Both throw down their shovels and stand waiting. The* WOMAN *sinks to a kneeling position on the sand, still holding the* CHILD. OLD GENTLEMAN *shouts as he comes near; his voice is high and thin. He is very old now, and is supported by two* MANSERVANTS. *His beard flies in the wind.*)

OLD GENTLEMAN. You foolish children! You leave the safety of my walls and come back to this dangerous shore, as your father did before you! The big wave will return and sweep you into the sea.

FIRST MAN. It may not, Ancient Sir.

OLD GENTLEMAN. It will come. I have spent my whole life trying to save foolish people from the big wave. But you will not be saved.

JIYA (*stepping forward*). Sir, here is our home. Dangerous as it is, threatened by the volcano and the sea, it is here we were born.

OLD GENTLEMAN (*looking at him*). Don't I know you?

JIYA. Sir, I was once in your castle.

OLD GENTLEMAN (*nodding*). I remember you. I wanted you for my son. Ah, you made a great mistake, young man. You could have lived safely in my castle all your life, and your children would have been safe there. The big wave never reaches me.

KINO. Sir, your castle is not safe, either. If the earth shakes hard enough, even your castle will crumble. There is no refuge for us who live on these islands. We are brave because we must be.

SECOND MAN. Ha—you are right.

(*The two* MEN *return to their building.*)

OLD GENTLEMAN (*rolling his eyes and wagging his beard*). Don't ask me to save you the next time the big wave comes!

JIYA (*gently*). But you will save us, because you are so good.

OLD GENTLEMAN (*looking at him and then smiling sadly*). What a pity you would not be my son! (*He turns and, leaning on his* MANSERVANTS, *climbs the mountain.*)

(FADE TO: *His arrival at the castle gate. He enters, and the gates clang shut.*)

(DISSOLVE TO: *The field where* FATHER *and* JIYA *and* KINO *are working.*)

FATHER (*to* JIYA). Did you soak the seeds for the rice?

JIYA (*aghast*). I forgot.

KINO. I did it.

JIYA (*throwing down his hoe*). I forget everything these days.

FATHER. I know you are too good a son to be forgetful on purpose. Tell me what is on your mind.

JIYA. I want a boat. I want to go back to fishing.

(FATHER *does not pause in his hoeing; but* KINO *flings down his hoe.*)

KINO. You, too, are foolish!

JIYA (*stubbornly*). When I have a boat, I shall build my own house on the beach.

KINO. Oh, fool, fool!

FATHER. Be quiet! Jiya is a man. You are both men. I shall pay you wages from this day.

JIYA. Wages! (*He falls to hoeing vigorously.*)

(DISSOLVE TO: *The beach, where the two young men are inspecting a boat.*)

JIYA. I knew all the time that I had to come back to the sea.

KINO. With this boat, you'll soon earn enough to build a house. But I'm glad I live on the mountain.

(*They continue inspecting the boat, fitting the oars, etc., as they talk.*)

JIYA (*abruptly*). Do you think Setsu would be afraid to live on the beach?

KINO (*surprised*). Why should Setsu live on the beach?

JIYA (*embarrassed but determined*). Because when I have my house built, I want Setsu to be my wife.

KINO (*astonished*). Setsu? You would be foolish to marry her.

THE BIG WAVE 159

JIYA (*smiling*). I don't agree with you.

KINO (*seriously*). But why—why do you want her?

JIYA. Because she makes me laugh. It is she who made me forget the big wave. For me, she is life.

KINO. But she is not a good cook. Think how she burns the rice when she runs outside to look at something.

JIYA. I don't mind burned rice, and I will run out with her to see what she sees.

KINO (*with all the gestures of astonishment and disbelief*). I can't understand. . . .

(DISSOLVE TO: *The farmhouse, and* FATHER *who is looking over his seeds.*)

KINO (*coming in stealthily*). Do you know that Jiya wants to marry Setsu?

FATHER. I have seen some looks pass between them.

KINO. But Jiya is too good for Setsu.

FATHER. Setsu is very pretty.

KINO. With that silly nose?

FATHER (*calmly*). I believe that Jiya admires her nose.

KINO. Besides, she is such a tease.

FATHER. What makes you miserable will make him happy.

KINO. I don't understand that, either.

FATHER (*laughing*). Someday you will understand.

(DISSOLVE TO: NARRATOR.)

NARRATOR. One day, one early summer, Jiya and Setsu were married. Kino still did not understand, for up to the last, Setsu was naughty and mischievous. Indeed on the very day of her wedding she hid Kino's hairbrush under his bed. "You are too silly to be married," Kino said when he had found it. "I feel sorry for Jiya," he said. Setsu's big brown eyes laughed at him, and she stuck out her red tongue. "I shall always be nice to Jiya," she said.

But when the wedding was over and the family had taken the newly married pair down the hill to the new house on the beach, Kino felt sad. The farmhouse was very quiet without Setsu. Already he missed her. Every day he could go to see Jiya, and many times he would be fishing with him. But Setsu would not be in the farmhouse kitchen, in the rooms, in the garden. He would miss even her teasing. And then he grew very grave indeed. What if the big wave came again?

(DISSOLVE TO: *The new house.* KINO *turns to* JIYA.)

KINO. Jiya, it is all very pretty—very nice. But, Setsu—what if the big wave comes again?

JIYA. I have prepared for that. Come—all of you. (*He calls the family in.*) This is where we will sleep at night, and where we will live by day. But look—

(*The family stands watching, and* JIYA *pushes back a long panel in the wall. Before their eyes is the sea, swelling and stirring under the evening wind. The sun is sinking into the water.*)

JIYA. I have opened my house to the sea. If ever the big wave comes back, I shall be ready. I face it, night and day. I am not afraid.

KINO. Tomorrow I'll go fishing with you, Jiya—shall I?

JIYA (*laughing*). Not tomorrow, brother!

(SETSU *comes to his side and leans against him, and he puts his arm about her.*)

FATHER. Yes, life is stronger than death. (*He turns to his family.*) Come, let us go home.

(FATHER *and* MOTHER *and* KINO *bow and leave.* JIYA *and* SETSU *stand looking out to the sea.*)

JIYA. Life is stronger than death—do you hear that, Setsu?

SETSU. Yes. I hear.

(*Curtain*)

TALKING ABOUT THE PLAY

1. Why do Kino and Jiya have different attitudes toward the sea as an enemy? Does Kino's life as a farmer's son affect his attitude? What influences Jiya's attitude? Why does the Old Gentleman always watch the sea? From this action, what can you learn about his attitude toward the sea? What is important about the statement that "No fisherman wants windows to the sea"?

2. How does nature forecast a warning of trouble for the people in the village? What action is taken by the Old Gentleman to warn the people? How does Jiya's father heed the warning? What happens to Jiya's family because of his father's action?

3. The big wave changes the lives of all the people in the play. Whose life is most affected by the big wave? How does Kino's family help Jiya? What does Kino learn about life during the time of Jiya's illness?

4. What proposal does the Old Gentleman offer Jiya? What kind of person is the Old Gentleman? Why does he offer the proposal to Jiya rather than to someone else? How does Kino feel about the proposal? What decision does Jiya make? Do you think Jiya's decision is a wise one? How does this decision affect Kino and Setsu?

5. Why does Jiya decide to go back to the life of the sea? Do you think Kino understands Jiya's feeling toward the sea? What clues in the play tell you that Jiya would be very happy married to Setsu and living near the sea? The window to the sea in Jiya's house shows a change in his attitude toward the sea and toward life. What is his new attitude? How does his new attitude differ from his old attitude? What do you think contributed to this change?

6. Sometimes the title of a play gives information about

either the plot or the main idea. What information did the title of this play give you? What other possible titles can you think of for this play? How might your different titles affect a reader?

7. How does the author show Japanese life so that it seems real and interesting to you? What scenes, lines of dialogue, or details provide especially close personal views of Japanese life?

8. The event of the big wave happens early in the play. You might think that this would be the high point or climax of the play, but it is not. What do you think is the climax of the play? How does the big wave lead up to the high point of the play?

9. What character is used by the playwright to tie together changes in scene and time? How might the author have developed the play without using this character?

10. Upon first seeing the title and reading a few scenes, you might think the mood of this play is one of gloom and sorrow. When you finished the play, though, you knew the mood was not hopeless but hopeful. What actions, lines, and ideas help to create this hopeful mood?

11. Many characters are used in the development of the plot although not all characters are important or major ones. Which do you think are major characters in this play? Why are they important? How does the author give you clues to their importance?

FOR YOUR OWN WRITING

1. A hurricane, earthquake, blizzard, or other natural disaster always commands a large amount of coverage by newspapers and magazines. Pretend you are a reporter in Japan at the time of the big wave. Write an eyewitness report describing the disaster in detail.

2. Suppose Jiya had accepted the Old Gentleman's offer. Write a composition about Jiya's life in the castle.
3. People usually wonder about the future. At the end of the play, you probably wondered what happened to Kino, Jiya, and Setsu as they lived out their lives by the sea. Write a short story describing what you think happened to them.

ABOUT THE PLAYWRIGHTS

Jerome Lawrence (1915–   ) and **Robert E. Lee** (1918–
) are writers of many distinguished and popular plays.
Their prize-winning *Inherit the Wind* ran three years on
Broadway and has been translated into 27 languages. Their
Auntie Mame had five companies running simultaneously in
the United States, and has been played in the major capitals
of the world. Both plays have been made into motion pictures.
Their other plays include *Look, Ma, I'm Dancin'*; *The Gang's
All Here*; *Only in America*; and *Sparks Fly Upward*. Early
in their careers, Lawrence and Lee wrote *Inside a Kid's
Head* for the Columbia Workshop, a famous radio program
at that time. Since then, *Inside a Kid's Head* has been published in a number of books and magazines.

Lawrence recently became a Doctor of Humane Letters at
Ohio State University, and Lee a Doctor of Literature at Ohio
Wesleyan. The two men have won numerous prizes, among
them the coveted Peabody Award twice. They are the co-
founders of the vast Armed Forces Radio Service, for which
they wrote and directed the world-wide broadcasts for D-Day,
V-E Day, and V-J Day. The team continues to write plays of
ideas, as well as to teach and lecture around the world, both
independently and for the State Department cultural exchange
program.

Nathaniel Hawthorne (1804–1864), famous American writer
of short stories and novels, was born in Salem, Massachusetts,
and lived there until 1836. Many of the stories written during
his early years appeared later in the book *Twice-Told Tales*.

With the help of his college classmate Franklin Pierce,
Hawthorne applied in 1837 for the post of historian to an
Antarctic expedition. He did not get the job, though, and
instead became a weigher in the Boston Custom House. In

1842 Hawthorne moved to Concord, Massachusetts, and continued to write short stories, many of which were published in the book *Mosses from an Old Manse*. In 1845 he went to Salem and became surveyor of the thriving port.

The Scarlet Letter, published in 1850, was well received, and 2000 copies were reportedly sold during the first ten days after publication. *The House of the Seven Gables* followed. It earned Hawthorne some money and a wider reputation. In 1852 his old friend Franklin Pierce—now President of the United States—appointed him United States Consul in Liverpool, England. While in Europe, Hawthorne traveled extensively, gathering material for books. He remained in Europe for seven years. In 1860 he published *The Marble Faun*, and in 1863 he published *Our Old Home*. Both books were based on his European material.

Hawthorne also wrote short stories and books for children. *A Wonder Book* and *Tanglewood Tales*, his retellings of Greek Myths, are read by many children today.

Willis Richardson (1889–   ) born in Wilmington, North Carolina, was the first American Negro to have a serious play produced on the Broadway stage. The play was *The Chip Woman's Fortune*, and was presented in 1923. Mr. Richardson's work since that time has been published in anthologies and magazines. An honorary citizen of Boy's Town, Mr. Richardson is also a member of the National Association for the Advancement of Colored People, the Christophers, and the Author's League of America. He is included in *Who's Who in the East* (1942) and *Who's Who in Colored America*.

Mr. Richardson was the winner of the first two Crisis-Springarn Play Prizes: *The Broken Banjo* in 1925 and *The Bootblack Lover* in 1926. He was the winner of the Edith Fisher Schwab Cup at Yale University Theater for *The Broken Banjo* in 1928.

Employed by the United States Bureau of Engraving and Printing in Washington, D.C., for forty-three years, he is now retired and living with his wife Mary Ellen and his four children in the nation's capital. Mr. Richardson has long been active in the struggle for racial equality in the religious, social, and economic areas of our nation.

Arthur Miller (1915–   ) was born and raised in New York and attended the University of Michigan. After graduation, he wrote a number of radio plays, including *Grandpa and the Statue*. He reported on World War II army camps in his book *Situation Normal* and exposed religious prejudice in his novel *Focus*. While he was married to the actress Marilyn Monroe, he wrote the screenplay for the movie *The Misfits*, in which she starred.

But Arthur Miller is best known for his stage plays. His most famous plays are *All My Sons, Death of a Salesman, The Crucible, A View from the Bridge, After the Fall,* and *Incident at Vichy*. The subjects of his plays have included family situations, immigration, concentration camps, and the Salem witch trials. He has received many awards, including Pulitzer Prizes and New York City Drama Critics' Circle Awards, for his plays. His plays are widely produced, and many of them have been made into motion pictures. His newest plays have already drawn audiences in France, Italy, Israel, Australia, and many other nations. Recently, four of his plays were performed professionally in one season in New York theatres.

John Van Druten (1901–1957) was born and educated in London, England. After receiving his law degree in 1922, he became a lecturer in English law at the University College of Wales. While busy with his law work and teaching, he also found time to write short stories, poems, and articles.

John Van Druten's association with the United States started soon after he wrote the play *Young Woodley* in 1925. This play was first performed in New York because its subject—life in an English school—was then considered too controversial for performance in London. Mr. Van Druten visited the United States frequently and decided in 1944 to become a naturalized American citizen. In 1944 he also wrote *I Remember Mama*, using material from Kathryn Forbes' popular book, *Mama's Bank Account*. After its successful stage production, *I Remember Mama* was made into a movie and expanded into a weekly television program.

As his plays became successful, Mr. Van Druten gave up his teaching career and devoted his time to writing. Among his other famous plays are *The Voice of the Turtle*; *The Druid Circle*; *Bell, Book and Candle*; and *I Am a Camera*. This last play won the New York Drama Critics' Circle Award in 1952.

John Van Druten directed many of his own dramas.

Milton Geiger (1907–   ) practiced pharmacy for several years while cultivating his taste for writing. Because he believes that a person should write about the things he understands best, his first radio plays were about medicine and pharmacy, and even *In the Fog* reveals something of the author's background. The idea for the play came, indeed, while the author was driving through the Pennsylvania hills late at night, in a heavy fog.

Milton Geiger is the author of hundreds of radio and television plays, many of them published, as well as of radio-TV adaptations of books, plays, and short stories. He was represented in 1958 on Broadway by his play *Edwin Booth* starring Jose Ferrer. The play is still extensively performed around the country and has been seen in Mr. Geiger's own adaptation on CBS television. Mr. Geiger now spends most of his time in Hollywood writing for television and films.

represented in 1958 on Broadway by his play *Edwin Booth* starring Jose Ferrer. The play is still extensively performed around the country and has been seen in Mr. Geiger's own adaptation on CBS television. Mr. Geiger now spends most of his time in Hollywood writing for television and films.

Pearl Buck (1892–   ) grew up in China, the daughter of American missionaries. Even as a child, she won literary prizes in the juvenile edition of the *Shanghai Mercury* and wanted to be a writer. Her mother taught her until she was 15, when she attended boarding school in Shanghai. At 17, she traveled to Europe and then to America for her college education. She then returned to China and taught English literature at universities in Nanking. She later moved to New York and married the president of a publishing company.

Pearl Buck is best known for her novels about Chinese people. Her book *The Good Earth* won the Pulitzer Prize and other awards in 1932, was translated into nearly twenty languages, and was both dramatized and filmed. This book, with her later work, brought her the Nobel Prize for Literature in 1938. She translated the Chinese classic *Shui Hu Chuan* as *All Men Are Brothers*. She wrote *Fighting Angel* and *The Exile*, two popular biographies of her parents. In *My Several Worlds* and other writings, she tells of her own experiences. She has written about particular social problems, such as the need for adoption of orphan children. She has also written TV plays, one Broadway play, and many other novels and stories on both Asian and American subjects, as well as a children's book on the big wave. Because of her experiences in different countries, she is uniquely qualified to describe Asian life to American readers. She is deeply concerned for people of all nations and races. She has six children, four of them adopted, and now lives on a farm in Pennsylvania.

a Kid's Head is subject to a royalty. It is fully protected under the copyright laws of the United States of America, of all countries covered by the International Copyright Union (including the Dominion of Canada and the rest of the British Commonwealth), of all countries covered by the Pan-American Copyright Convention and the Universal Copyright Convention, and of all countries with which the United States has reciprocal copyright relations. All rights, including professional, amateur, motion pictures, television, lecturing, public reading, radio broadcasting, and the rights of translation into foreign languages, are strictly reserved. Permission in writing and a payment of royalty must be made. All inquiries should be addressed to the playwrights at 18106 Malibu Road, Malibu, California, United States of America 90265.

William Morris Agency, Inc.: For an excerpt from *I Remember Mama*, by John Van Druten.

CAUTION: Professionals and amateurs are hereby warned that *I Remember Mama* being fully protected under the copyright laws of the United States of America, the British Empire including the Dominion of Canada, and all other countries of the copyright union, is subject to royalty. All rights including professional, amateur, motion picture, recitation, lecturing, public reading, radio broadcasting, television and the rights of translation into foreign languages are strictly reserved. All inquiries (other than amateur rights) should be addressed to the author's representative, William Morris Agency, 1740 Broadway, New York, New York 10019.

The amateur acting rights of this play are controlled exclusively by Dramatists Play Service, Inc., 440 Park Avenue South, New York, New York, without whose permission in writing no amateur performance of it may be made. Copyright 1952 and 1955, by John Van Druten. All rights reserved.

Harold Ober Associates, Inc.: For *The Big Wave*, by Pearl S. Buck. Original story copyright 1947 by The Curtis Publishing Company. Copyright 1948 by Pearl S. Buck. Television play copyright 1948 by Pearl S. Buck. Based on the book of the same title published by The John Day Company.

CAUTION: All rights reserved. Applications for performance of this play by professional and amateur companies in all parts of the world should be made to Harold Ober Associates Incorporated, 40 East 49th Street, New York, New York 10017, who have granted permission for the reprinting.

Willis Richardson: For *Attucks, the Martyr*. Reprinted by permission of Willis Richardson.

For assistance in preparing this manuscript, the editor wishes to thank Miss Barbara Harr.